KEY GUIDE
To
AUSTRALIAN
TREES

Pittosporum undulatum

KEY GUIDE
To
AUSTRALIAN TREES

LEONARD CRONIN

Illustrated by
JENNY TARANTO
MARION WESTMACOTT

REED

ACKNOWLEDGEMENTS

Special thanks to Robert Kooyman for sharing
his expert knowledge, helping to compile the species' list
and locating and identifying many of the trees.
To Madelaine Faught and Karen Taranto who supplied
an important part of the photographic reference
material. To Anna Hallett of the National Herbarium
of NSW for her patience and help in providing
reference material and Barbara Wiecek for checking
the species' nomenclature; and to the Librarian
and staff of the State Library of NSW.

REED BOOKS
a division of
Reed International Books
North Tower, Chatswood Plaza,
1-5 Railway St. Chatswood, NSW 2067
First published 1988
Reprinted 1989
Reprinted 1992

Planned and produced by
LEONARD CRONIN

Research by
GERTRUD LATOUR

© Leonard Cronin 1988

National Library of Australia
Cataloguing-in-Publication data

Cronin, Leonard.
Key Guide to Australian Trees.

Bibliography.
Includes index.
ISBN 0 7301 0252 1
1. Trees – Identification. 1. Title.
(Series: Key Guides to Australian Flora)

582.160994

Typeset by Deblaere Typesetting Pty Ltd

Printed in Hong Kong

CONTENTS

INTRODUCTION

Trees and their products are an integral part of our lives. We use them to build our houses and furniture, to make our newspapers and books, we exploit their chemical products to make rubber, petrol, plastics and medicines. Songs, poems and prose in every language eulogise the beauty of their flowers and foliage, their fruits and their deep, restful shade. Trees support countless numbers of animals and plants. They are one of the greatest primary producers on earth, supplying our oxygen, moderating the climate and even filtering some of our industrial wastes. Without trees our species might not even exist, and certainly our civilisations would be vastly different.

We use their products and are familiar with many of their names, but to accurately identify the trees themselves can be quite difficult. Surprisingly, considering our dependence on trees, reliable books describing the Australian species are thin on the ground. Few have a key to help the observer identify an unknown species, and most are lacking in good colour illustrations.

This book has been designed as a practical field guide for both the casual observer and the dedicated botanist. A simple visual key directs the reader to pages of the book where trees with similar characteristics are illustrated and described.

Specially commissioned watercolour illustrations have been carefully executed by two of Australia's foremost botanical illustrators to show the most important identifiable characteristics of all the 249 trees included. The descriptions are in a consistent, easily-understood style with the minimum use of botanical terminology, and include all the major visible characteristics of the trees: their size, shape and form, bark, leaves, flowers, fruits, flowering times, habitat and family. The few botanical terms used are explained in the glossary at the end of the book.

The species described are those commonly encountered in Nature Reserves, National Parks and along the roadsides throughout Australia. Some are included because of their unusual and distinctive characteristics, and although these might not be so common, their beautiful flowers, unusual fruits or strange shapes are certain to attract the attention of even the most casual observer.

Trees often vary in size and general appearance according to their environment. A tree growing in a closed forest may grow very tall with a small compact crown as it strives for the sunlight, whereas the same species growing in an open paddock may be much lower with a wide, spreading crown. Soils and climates also affect the size and shape of trees, and these variations should be taken into account when using the book.

The Latin names given are currently accepted by the scientific community, and the synonyms in parentheses are superceded names still to be found in the literature. Common names are also included because most people are more comfortable and familiar with these, and many find the pronunciation of Latin names difficult.

Identification is the first major step towards a greater appreciation and understanding of our natural environment. Like faces in a crowd, once we know their names trees stand out as individuals, we feel more empathy with the familiar and care more for their well-being. And today our trees and forests need all the help they can get.

Trees represent the largest and longest-living life forms on earth. Many are identical to those browsed upon by the strange animals that millions of years ago roamed lands presently covered by our own creations of glass, concrete and stone. These species have survived dramatic changes in the environment only to fall prey to the woodchopper's axe, chainsaws and bulldozers of modern man.

As our cities and territorial claims expand we dominate more and more of the ecology of this planet and find ourselves increasingly isolated in our own artificially created environments. We are, in fact, becoming strangers on our own planet, unfamiliar with the very species we are so dependent upon. But whether we like it or not we remain just a small part of an intertwined and delicately balanced biological system, and at the very heart of that system are the trees: a fundamental biological unit about which terrestrial life on this planet revolves.

Our record since European settlement in Australia demonstrates a callous disregard for this web of life. We have carried out a ruthless policy of destruction, reducing our great forests to marginal farmlands, sacrificing millions of years of evolutionary advances on the altar of economic progress. Little wonder that our children are not taught and encouraged to familiarise themselves with the forests and rainforests, to know the names and appreciate the beauty, grandeur and irreplaceable value of the different trees growing there; because they may have no untouched forests and rain-forests to visit, and the many hundreds of tree species will have been reduced to those few considered to be of economic or ornamental use.

The time left to us to conserve the balance of nature has almost run out. Those who claim that the continued destruction of our forests will have no serious impact on our environment, and those who believe that the balance can be restored by replanting selected economical species are sadly mistaken. The very nature of life on earth depends upon variety. Where we would plant one species nature would establish one thousand. It is foolish arrogance to believe that we can take control of the environment and maintain a viable ecological system. We are experts in destruction, not in creation or even conservation.

But conservation is something we *must* learn, and if this book plays a small part in this learning process by helping us to become more familiar with the wonderful beauty and variety of our forests and woodlands, then its purpose will have been achieved.

HOW TO USE THIS GUIDE

To use this book you do not need any knowledge of plant classification. The following visual keys direct you to pages where trees with similar leaf shapes are gathered together, or in the case of the eucalypts, where those with similar fruits are gathered together.

For the non-eucalypts, simply compare a typical mature leaf from the tree you wish to identify with the **General leaf shape** shown in the left hand column of the first two **Key Guide** pages. Having found the nearest corresponding **General leaf shape** look at the centre column to find the nearest **Typical leaf shape**. Now simply turn to the pages indicated and identify the tree by looking at the illustrations and descriptions given. Samples of the flowers and fruits will help you to make an accurate identification.

The eucalypts are by far the most common and distinctive trees in Australia, and share the following characteristics:

1. The mature leaves are typically drooping, tough and leathery, narrow lanceolate to sickle-shaped with a distinct stalk and a characteristic eucalypt smell when crushed.

2. The flower buds are covered by a cap which is shed allowing the many long stamens of the flower to emerge.

3. The fruits are woody capsules with small enclosed or protruding valves.

The **Key Guide: Eucalypts** on page 12 is based on the shape of the fruits, which are usually found around the base of the tree or on low branches.

EXAMPLE 1: NON-EUCALYPTS

In a coastal woodland area of NSW you find a small gnarled and twisted tree with spongy dark grey bark, leathery leaves with serrated margins, cylindrical silver-grey flowering spikes and grey cylindrical fruiting cones.

1. Using the **Key Guide: Non-Eucalypts** you find that the **Toothed** leaf shape in the left hand column resembles the generalised shape of the leaves.

2. In the centre column the **Toothed spathulate** shape closely resembles a typical leaf from the tree, and you are referred to pages 86, 106-108.

3. On page 108 you find that the illustration and description of *Banksia serrata* match the tree.

EXAMPLE 2: EUCALYPTS

In an open forest along the Victorian coast you discover a tall eucalypt with cream-coloured flowers, urn-shaped fruits with enclosed valves, and red gum exuding from the brown-barked trunk.

1. Using the **Key Guide Eucalypts** you find in the left hand column fruit with **Enclosed valves**

2. Moving to the centre column you find that your specimen closely resembles the **Urn-shaped** fruit depicted, and that you are referred to pages 140-146, 160.

3. On page 142 you find that the illustration and description of *Eucalyptus gummifera* match the tree.

KEY GUIDE: NON EUCALYPTS

General leaf shape	Typical leaf shape		Page
Narrow cylindrical		Scale-leaf	14-18
		Needle-leaf	18-26
Lanceolate		Narrow lanceolate	26-46
		Broad lanceolate	48-62
Broad		Spathulate	84-90
		Ovate	62-84 90 94
		Elliptical	64-84 100 118
		Heart-shaped	84 90-92 118

KEY GUIDE: NON EUCALYPTS

General leaf shape	Typical leaf shape		Page
Toothed		Toothed lanceolate	98-104 110
		Toothed spathulate	86 106-108
		Toothed ovate	90-98
		Lobed	100 116-120
		Trifoliolate	110-114 122
		Palmate	112-116
		Pinnate	26 120-132
		Bipinnate	134-138

KEY GUIDE: EUCALYPTS

General fruit shape	Typical fruit shape		Page
Protruding valves		Conical	148-150
		Pear-shaped	150-152 156 166 172
		Cup-shaped	156-158 162
		Spherical	162 166 172-174
		Urn-shaped	148
		Ribbed	176
Enclosed valves		Ribbed	140 176-178
		Conical	146 154 158
		Pear-shaped	152-154 164 168
		Cup-shaped	156-164
		Spherical	164 168-170
		Urn-shaped	140-146 160

Colour Plates
And
Tree Descriptions

Exocarpos cupressiformis   NATIVE CHERRY. CHERRY BALLART

A tall shrub or small tree, 3-8 m high with a short trunk somewhat flanged at the base, a dense cypress-like crown and slender usually pendulous branches. **Bark** is dark grey, rough, finely fissured and easily detached. **Mature leaves** are reduced to a few tiny scales, and the pale green, fine and faintly ribbed branchlets carry out photosynthesis. **Flowers** are cream to green, very small, open, about 1 mm across with 5 lobes, arranged in small axillary or terminal spikes 3-6 mm long on stiff green stalks. **Fruits** are hard green globular nuts 5-6 mm diameter attached to a yellow to red succulent, edible receptacle about 1 cm long. **Flowering** mainly in summer and autumn. **Habitat.** Common in moist open forests at various altitudes on shallow soils in Qld, NSW, Vic., SA, WA and Tas. **Family.** Santalaceae.

Athrotaxis selaginoides   KING WILLIAM PINE

A medium-sized to tall tree to 40 m high with a long fluted, often buttressed or forked trunk to 1.8 m diameter, stunted and twisted in high exposed sites, with a relatively small densely tufted crown with many branches, and the branchlets often arranged in 2 vertical rows. **Bark** is reddish-brown, weathering to grey-brown, persistent, thick, spongy and slightly fibrous with longitudinal furrows. **Mature leaves** are scale-like, thick, narrow with a sharp point, to 12 mm long, slightly curved and crowded in loosely overlapping spirals around the branchlets. **Cones.** Male and female cones are borne on the same tree. Male cones resemble catkins. Female cones are spherical with spirally arranged scales, borne at the ends of short shoots. They are green turning brown and woody when mature, 12-20 mm diameter, with numerous pointed scales each bearing up to 6 oblong winged seeds on the undersurface; maturing in winter and spring. **Habitat.** Valley slopes and floors to 1400 m in small stands in cool temperate rainforests in Tas. **Family.** Taxodiaceae.

Araucaria cunninghamii   HOOP PINE

A tall tree to 60 m high with a straight cylindrical trunk to 1.9 m diameter, more or less horizontal branches whorled around the trunk with tufts of leaves clustered at the ends, forming a symmetrical crown. **Bark** is dark greyish-brown, hard and rough with horizontal cracks forming hoops around the trunk. **Mature leaves** are scale-like, narrow and triangular, 3-15 mm long with a sharp point, slightly curved and crowded in spirals around the branchlets. **Cones.** Separate male and female cones are borne on the same tree. Male cones are light brown, very small and densely packed into terminal cylindrical spikes 4-8 cm long. Female cones are packed into terminal cylindrical spikes 4-8 cm long. Female cones are green, ovoid, about 12 mm diameter, composed of numerous bracts and borne at the ends of branchlets near the top of the tree. They turn brown and woody in summer and autumn, becoming 7-10 cm across and splitting on the tree into numerous flat, wedge-shaped winged seeds about 1 cm long. **Habitat.** Poorer soils in rainforests, rocky gorges and along stream banks of the coast and tablelands in northern NSW and Qld. **Family.** Araucariaceae.

Exocarpos cupressiformis

Athrotaxis selaginoides

Araucaria cunninghamii

M. Westmacott

Callitris rhomboidea   PORT JACKSON OR OYSTER BAY PINE

A tall bushy shrub or small tree, 2-6 m high with a slender trunk and a bushy, columnar or conical crown with drooping branchlets. **Bark** is thin, brown to greenish brown. **Mature leaves** are dark green, sometimes covered with a silvery bloom, reduced to tiny scales 2-4 mm long with a keel at the back, arranged in alternating whorls of 3 sheathing the coarse angular branchlets. **Cones** are globular, about 2 cm across, dark brown and woody, smooth initially but drying out to become wrinkled and dark, with a large conical projection on each of the 6 alternating segments (scales). These are joined at their bases and open to release numerous small winged seeds. The cones are solitary or clustered at the ends of the branches. **Habitat.** Usually found in large colonies in low open forests on rocky slopes, sandy hills and plains along the coast and nearby ranges of all states except NT and WA. **Family.** Cupressaceae.

Callitris endlicheri   BLACK CYPRESS PINE

A small to medium-sized tree, 5-20 m high with a straight cylindrical trunk and a dense slender dark green cypress-like crown, occasionally with spreading branches. **Bark** is dark reddish-brown and coarsely furrowed. **Mature leaves** are dark green, sometimes bluish, reduced to tiny scales 2-4 mm long with a keel at the back, arranged in alternating whorls of 3 sheathing the coarse angular branchlets. **Cones** are globular, about 2 cm across, dark brown and woody at maturity, smooth with a small sharp projection near the tip of each of the 6 alternating large and small segments (scales), joined at the base and opening to release numerous small winged seeds. They are terminal or clustered at the ends of small branchlets. **Habitat.** Common on drier sites on rocky outcrops and well-drained sandy soils on stony hills of the tablelands, slopes and plains in southern Qld, NSW and northeastern Vic. **Family.** Cupressaceae.

Callitris preissii   ROTTNEST ISLAND OR SLENDER CYPRESS PINE

Small to medium-sized tree 5-20 m high with a slender trunk about 50 cm diameter and a dense dark green rounded crown on well-formed trees. **Bark** is dark grey, fibrous, irregularly fissured and persistent to the small branches. **Mature leaves** are dark green, reduced to tiny scales 2-4 mm long arranged in alternating whorls of 3, sheathing the needle-like green branchlets. **Cones** are spherical to ovoid, dark brown and woody at maturity, commonly with scattered warty projections. They comprise 3 large and 3 smaller alternating segments (scales) united at their bases on stout stalks. The larger scales are blunt-tipped, the smaller ones pointed. The cones are 25-30 cm across and open when mature to release numerous small light brown seeds with 2 broad wings; they often persist on the tree for years. **Habitat.** Common on sand dunes and sandy soils near sea level in mallee regions, forming woodlands in NSW, Vic., SA and WA. **Family.** Cupressaceae.

Callitris rhomboidea

Callitris endlicheri

Callitris preissii

Callitris glaucophylla (syn. Callitris glauca)   WHITE CYPRESS PINE

Small to medium-sized tree, 7-30 m high, with a straight trunk, usually about 45 cm diameter. It has a fairly dense conical crown in woodlands although it may be flat-topped in dense stands. **Bark** is dark grey, hard and persistent to the small branches, deeply furrowed and pinkish brown on newly exposed areas. **Mature leaves** are green to grey-green, reduced to tiny scales 1-3 mm long and about 0.5 mm wide arranged in alternating whorls of 3, sheathing the needle-like green branchlets. **Cones** are spherical, dark brown and woody at maturity, with 3 large and 3 smaller alternating scales attached at their bases, wrinkled outside with a small point near the tip. They become 10-25 mm across and open to release numerous small, light brown, winged seeds. The cones fall from the tree after maturity. **Habitat.** Common in inland woodlands on rolling hills on a wide variety of soils, forming extensive forests in southern Qld and northern NSW, but occurring in all mainland states. **Family.** Cupressaceae.

Callitris macleayana   BRUSH CYPRESS PINE

A medium-sized to tall tree to 39 m high with a straight, slender trunk to 90 cm diameter, spreading branches and a fairly dense crown with fine textured light green foliage. **Bark** is grey to greyish-brown, stringy with vertical furrows, sometimes scaly and thick. Freshly cut bark has a resinous smell, and clear resin exudes from the cut surface of the tree. **Mature leaves** are needle-like, flat and rigid in young trees, about 6 mm long alternating in whorls of 3-4. They are reduced to scales or acute teeth in old trees, 3-6 mm long in whorls of 3 around angular branchlets. **Cones.** Both male and female cones are borne on the same tree. Male cones are light brown, oblong, 4-8 mm long and borne at the ends of the branchlets. Female cones are stalkless and found on short lateral branchlets. They are spherical and about 6 mm diameter, growing to 25-30 mm across at maturity when they are ovoid to conical or pyramidal, dark brown and woody, comprising 6 or 8 scales equal in length and pointed at their tips. They open in autumn and early winter to release numerous oval reddish-brown flattened winged seeds about 14 mm long. **Habitat.** Open forests and the fringes of warm temperate rainforests on poorer sandy soils along the coast and nearby ranges of southern Qld and northern NSW. **Family.** Cupressaceae.

Araucaria heterophylla   NORFOLK ISLAND PINE

A tall tree to 60 m high with a straight cylindrical trunk and whorled horizontal branches fairly widely spaced, giving an open symmetrical pyramid-shaped crown with ascending branchlets. **Bark** is dark brown, rough and somewhat scaly with numerous small blisters and circular scars of fallen branches whorled around the trunk. It exudes large quantities of resin when cut. **Mature leaves** are soft, leathery, stalkless, bright green and 5-10 mm long. They are triangular and scale-like, arranged in overlapping whorls to form ascending cylindrical branchlets 1-2 cm across and to 30 cm or more long. **Cones** are woody, green, globular and pineapple-like, 7-13 cm diameter, with spirally arranged scales attached to flattened wingless seeds. They are borne on short terminal shoots and disintegrate when mature to release the seeds. **Habitat.** A native of Norfolk Island, but widely planted as a coastal ornamental in eastern Qld and NSW, growing on very sandy soils and tolerant of sea spray. **Family.** Araucariaceae.

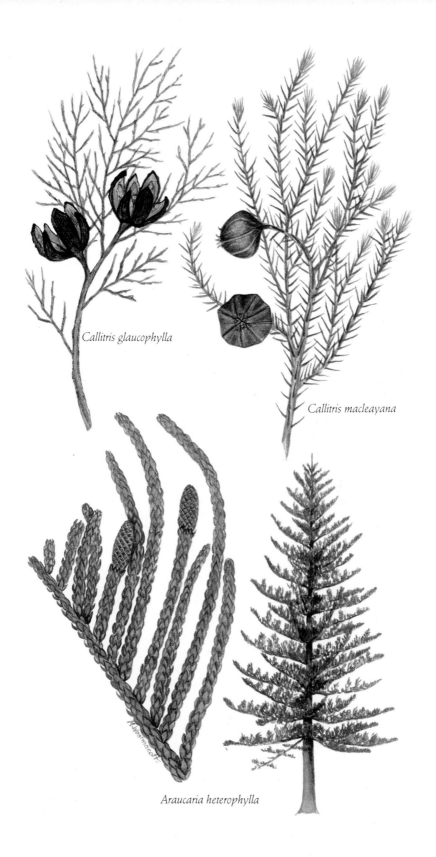

Callitris glaucophylla

Callitris macleayana

Araucaria heterophylla

Casuarina cunninghamiana   RIVER SHE-OAK

A medium-sized to tall tree, 12-35 m high with a straight trunk to 1.5 m diameter and a slender, conical crown with fine, pendulous branchlets. **Bark** is dark grey and hard, persistent over the trunk and branches, deeply furrowed with numerous conspicuous white, raised blisters on young trees. **Mature leaves** are minute 'teeth' with their tiny pointed tips in whorls of 6-10 at intervals of 4-9 mm along the needle-like dark green longitudinally grooved branchlets, 10-25 cm long and about 0.6 mm diameter; some branchlets are shed after 2-3 seasons. **Flowers** are light brown or red, very small and borne on separate male and female trees. Females are ovoid and hairy, in alternating whorls of 6-7 along the small branches. Males form short dense cylindrical spikes 1-2 cm long on the ends of the branchlets. **Fruits** are slightly flattened ovoid grey to brown woody cones about 1 cm long on short stalks, opening in short longitudinal slits to release winged brown seeds. **Flowering** in winter and spring. **Habitat.** Common along freshwater stream banks in open forests on both sides of the Great Dividing Range in Qld, NSW and NT. **Family.** Casuarinaceae.

Casuarina glauca   SWAMP OAK

A medium-sized tree 8-30 m high with a straight trunk to 75 cm diameter which may be slightly buttressed in older trees, and a dull grey-green crown of erect coarse branchlets. **Bark** is dark grey, hard and rough, persistent over the trunk and branches with shallow vertical and longitudinal furrows producing small squares; grey lichens grow on trees close to the water. **Mature leaves** are minute 'teeth' with their tiny pointed tips in whorls of 9-16 at intervals of 8-12 mm along the needle-like grey-green branchlets, to 30 cm long and about 1 mm diameter; some branchlets are shed after 2-3 seasons. **Flowers** are light brown or red, very small and borne on separate male and female trees. Females form globular and hairy spikes along the small branches. Males form cylindrical spikes 1-3 cm long on the ends of the branchlets. **Fruits** are cylindrical grey to brown woody cones with a flattened apex about 12 mm diameter on short stalks, opening in short longitudinal slits to release small, winged, brown seeds. **Flowering** in winter and spring. **Habitat.** Locally abundant in open forests and woodlands near saltwater estuaries and rivers near the coast of Qld and NSW. **Family.** Casuarinaceae.

Allocasuarina verticillata (syn. Casuarina stricta)   DROOPING SHE-OAK

A small, spreading tree to 11 m high with a straight trunk and a rounded crown of drooping rather coarse branchlets. **Bark** is dark grey, persistent, rough and furrowed. **Mature leaves** are minute 'teeth' with their tiny pointed tips in whorls of 9-12 at intervals of about 2 cm along the needle-like dark green ribbed branchlets, to 30 cm long and about 1 mm diameter. **Flowers** are brown or red, very small and borne on separate male and female trees. Females form globular and hairy spikes to about 1 cm across along the small branches. Males form cylindrical spikes 5-12 cm long on the ends of the branchlets or growing from the old wood. **Fruits** are ovoid grey to brown woody cones 2-5 cm long and 2-3 cm across on short stalks with prominent forward-pointing protruding valves, opening to release small brown winged seeds about 8 mm long. **Flowering** in winter and spring. **Habitat.** Common on exposed sites along coastal cliffs, dunes and rocky outcrops in NSW, Vic., SA and Tas. **Family.** Casuarinaceae.

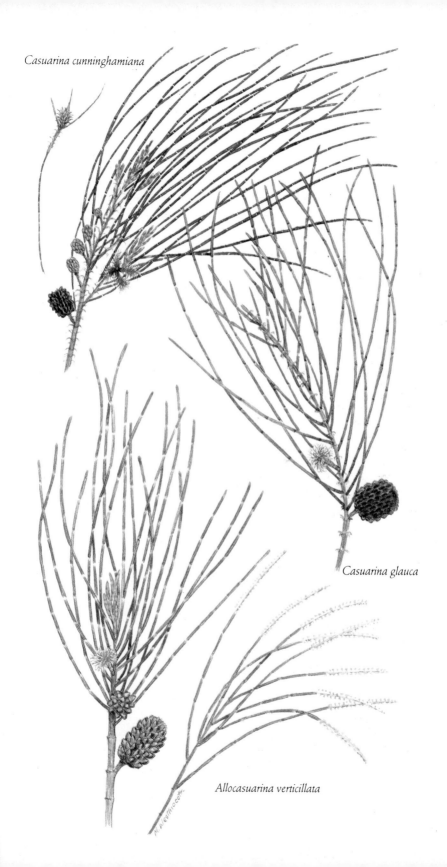

Casuarina cunninghamiana

Casuarina glauca

Allocasuarina verticillata

Allocasuarina distyla (syn. Casuarina d.)   SHRUB SHE-OAK

A large shrub to small tree, 2-5 m high with a straight, slender trunk and a fairly sparse crown. **Mature leaves** are minute 'teeth' in whorls at the joints of needle-like dark green photosynthetic ribbed branchlets, 10-20 cm long and about 1 mm diameter with the tiny pointed leaf tips in whorls of 6-8 at intervals of 5-8 mm. **Flowers** are reddish-brown, very small and borne on separate male and female trees. Females form globular and hairy spikes to about 1 cm across on the small branches. Males form cylindrical spikes 2-8 cm long on the ends of the branchlets. **Fruits** are cylindrical grey to brown woody cones 2-4 cm long and about 2 cm across on short stalks with numerous slightly protruding rounded valves, opening to release small brown winged seeds. **Flowering** in winter and spring. **Habitat.** Common and widespread on heaths and scrublands on sandy soils and old dunes along the coast of NSW. **Family.** Casuarinaceae.

Allocasuarina littoralis (syn. Casuarina l.)   BLACK SHE-OAK

A small tree, 4-14 m high with a straight, slender trunk and a fairly sparse, very dark green conical crown with erect branches. **Bark** is brown, hard and closely fissured. **Mature leaves** are minute 'teeth' in whorls at the joints of needle-like blackish-green photosynthetic ribbed and erect branchlets, about 10 cm long and 1 mm diameter with the tiny pointed leaf tips in whorls of 6-8 at intervals of 5-10 mm. **Flowers** are reddish-brown, very small and borne on separate male and female trees. Females form globular and hairy spikes to about 7 mm across on the older wood. Males form cylindrical spikes 1-3 cm long on the ends of the branchlets. **Fruits** are cylindrical grey to brown woody cones, slightly flattened at the ends, 2-3 cm long and 15-20 mm across on thick stalks about 2 cm long, with numerous prominent rounded valves, opening to release small brown winged seeds to 5 mm long. **Flowering** in autumn. **Habitat.** Widespread on heaths, forests and stony ridges, particularly on sandy soils along the coast of Qld, NSW, Vic. and Tas. **Family.** Casuarinaceae.

Allocasuarina torulosa (syn. Casuarina t.)   FOREST OAK. ROSE SHE-OAK

A medium-sized tree, 8-30 m high with a straight, slender trunk to 1.3 m diameter, and spreading branches with pendant foliage clumped at the ends to give an open crown. **Bark** is light brown to black, persistent over the trunk and main branches, closely furrowed vertically and transversally producing sharp corky ridges. **Mature leaves** are minute in whorls at the joints of needle-like dark green photosynthetic and longitudinally grooved branchlets. There are deciduous and permanent branchlets, the deciduous ones are often copper-coloured at the base; both are pendant, 5-8 cm long and about 0.6 mm diameter with the tiny pointed leaf tips in whorls of 4 at intervals of 3-6 mm. **Flowers** are light brown, very small and borne on separate male and female trees. Females are globular and hairy, in alternating whorls of usually 5 along the small branches. Males are grouped in whorls of usually 4, forming short cylindrical spikes 1-3 cm long on the ends of the branchlets. **Fruits** are globular to barrel-shaped grey to brown woody cones, 2-3 cm long on slender stalks 1-3 cm long, opening in short longitudinal slits to release winged brown seeds. **Flowering** in spring and summer. **Habitat.** Widespread in moist open forests along the coast and adjacent ranges in Qld and NSW. **Family.** Casuarinaceae.

Allocasuarina distyla

Allocasuarina littoralis

Allocasuarina torulosa

Viminaria juncea   GOLDEN SPRAY. NATIVE BROOM

An erect shrub to small tree, 2-5 m high with a slender cylindrical trunk, long slender drooping prickly branchlets and a sparse crown. **Bark** is greyish-brown, rough and fissured. **Mature leaves** are alternate needle-like phyllodes, 7-25 cm long and about 2 mm wide, bright green and wiry. **Flowers** are golden yellow, pea-shaped, 7-10 mm long with a notched standard petal with red markings near the base, arranged in long, slender, terminal, drooping racemes 25-60 cm long. **Fruits** are soft stalkless ovate pods, 4-6 mm long, containing a single hard seed. **Flowering** in spring and early summer. **Habitat.** Moist heaths on sandy soils and swampy sites of the coast and adjacent lower mountains in temperate areas of Qld, NSW, Vic., SA and Tas. **Family.** Papilionaceae.

Acacia verticillata   PRICKLY MOSES

An erect spreading shrub to small tree, 2-6 m high with a slender trunk, arching angular and ribbed branches and an open crown of prickly foliage. **Mature leaves** are whorled, needle-like, sharply pointed and sometimes flattened phyllodes, 8-25 mm long and 1-2 mm wide, stalkless, dull green and rigid with a prominent midrib. **Flowers** are bright yellow and crowded into fluffy ovoid or cylindrical heads 8-40 mm long on stalks 1-2 cm long, solitary or 2-3 together in the leaf axils. **Fruits** are flat straight or curved dark brown pods, 2-8 cm long and 3-4 mm wide, slightly thickened between the seeds. **Flowering** in winter, spring and early summer. **Habitat.** Common in heaths, scrubs and forests, preferring moist, well-drained sandy soils along the coast and foothills in southern NSW, Vic., SA and Tas. **Family.** Mimosaceae.

Pinus radiata   RADIATA OR MONTEREY PINE

A tall tree to 50 m high with a long straight cylindrical trunk to 90 cm diameter and a narrow irregular open crown. **Bark** is dark reddish-brown, thick and deeply furrowed with scaly ridges. **Mature leaves** are slender needles mostly in bundles of 3, 10-15 cm long and shiny dark green. **Cones.** Male and female cones are borne on the same tree. Male cones are yellow-green and cylindrical, about 1 cm long and arranged in clusters behind the new growth. Female cones are found at the ends of the branches. They are reddish-purple and about 1 cm long before fertilisation, becoming woody, shiny brown, conical to egg-shaped, 7-15 cm long and 6-10 cm diameter with whorls of slightly raised and rounded scales. They open when ripe after 2-3 years' maturation to release many small black winged seeds. **Habitat.** Introduced from California but naturalised and widely cultivated on sandy loams in NSW and Vic. **Family.** Pinaceae.

Viminaria juncea

Acacia verticillata

Pinus radiata

M.Westmacott

Kingia australis　　　　　DRUMHEAD BLACK BOY. SKIRTED GRASS TREE

A small tree-like plant to 6 m high with a slender cylindrical trunk to 40 cm diameter and a small tufted crown of long needle-like leaves. They are extremely slow growing and take many years to reach maturity. **Bark** is light-brown and fibrous with rings of the remnants of persistent packed leaf bases; often blackened by fire. **Mature leaves** are alternate, needle-like to narrow linear and 4-angled in section with a widely expanded base, to 60 cm long and 2-3 mm wide, silky and pale green; the dead leaves remain for some time, skirt-like around the top of the trunk. **Flowers** are creamy-white, open, with narrow lanceolate lobes 2-3 cm long, stalkless and packed into globular axillary heads about 6 cm across on thick, scaly, erect stalks 30-50 cm long. **Fruits** are black seeds produced singly and contained within the drying persistent flowers. **Flowering** mainly in winter and spring. **Habitat.** Widespread in sandy, gravelly or rocky soils in woodlands or heaths at various altitudes in the higher rainfall areas of southwestern WA. **Family.** Xanthorrhoeaceae.

Xanthorrhoea preissii　　　　　COMMON BLACK BOY. GRASS TREE

A small tree-like plant to 7 m high with a slender cylindrical trunk, sometimes divided near the top, and one or more small terminal tufted globular crowns of long needle-like leaves. They grow only about 1 m in 30 years. **Bark** is brown to grey-brown and fibrous with regular rings of the remnants of persistent packed leaf bases; often blackened by fire. **Mature leaves** are alternate, needle-like to narrow-linear, tapering to a sharp point, 4-angled in section with a thickened base, 60-120 cm long and 2-3 mm wide, green turning brown with age; the dead leaves form a skirt around the base of the crown. **Flowers** are creamy-white, about 1 cm across with 6 lobes and 6 protruding stamens, spirally arranged in clusters of 3 around a long cylindrical flowering spike to 3 m long and 3-6 cm diameter, pale green triangular bracts surround the flower clusters filling the space between them. **Fruits** are brown beaked capsules opening when ripe to release 1-2 black ovate seeds. **Flowering** is erratic, often after fire. **Habitat.** Widespread in southwestern WA. **Family.** Xanthorrhoeaceae.

Grevillea pteridifolia　　　　　FERN-LEAVED GREVILLEA

A tall shrub or small tree, 3-8 m high with a slender trunk and spreading erect soft hairy branches with an open crown of fern-like leaves. **Bark** is dark grey, becoming light grey to white on the young branches. **Mature leaves** are pinnately divided into long narrow needle-like segments 10-20 cm long. **Flowers** are golden orange and full of nectar, small and tubular with long protruding styles, arranged in dense terminal cylindrical racemes 10-20 cm long. **Fruits** are ovoid woody dark brown follicles about 2 cm long with a long narrow beak. **Flowering** in winter. **Habitat.** Widespread along the banks of freshwater swamps and creeks in the tropical areas of WA, NT and Qld. **Family.** Proteaceae.

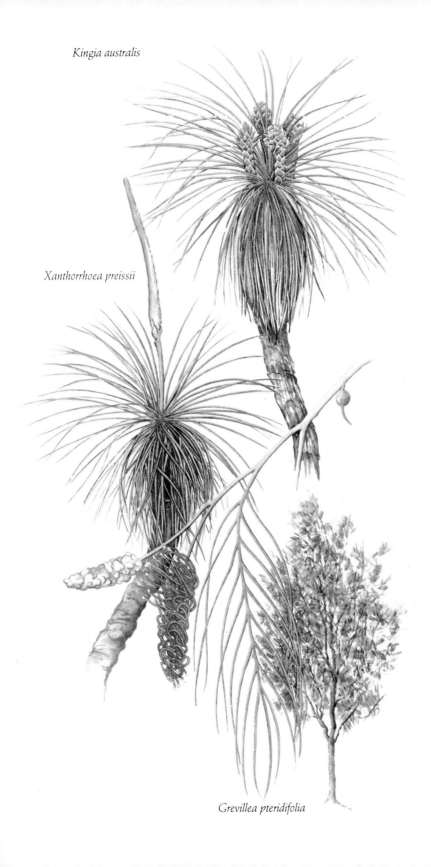

Kingia australis

Xanthorrhoea preissii

Grevillea pteridifolia

Notelaea longifolia (syn. N. venosa)   MOCK OR LONG-LEAVED OLIVE

A small tree to 9 m high, low branching with a short irregularly-shaped trunk to 30 cm diameter and a dense, widely-spreading crown. **Bark** is grey or greyish-brown, hard, rough, finely fissured and scaly in large trees; the branchlets have small raised spots. **Mature leaves** are opposite, narrow lanceolate to ovate, leathery, 5-15 cm long and 1-8 cm wide on stalks 1-8 mm long, dull dark green above and paler below, often covered with downy hairs, conspicuously veined with 6-8 lateral veins and irregular net veins. **Flowers** are white to pale yellow, small with 4 concave lobes and 2 stamens, arranged in short axillary racemes. **Fruits** are purplish-black fleshy, egg-shaped drupes, 10-16 mm long, containing a single egg-shaped seed 8-12 mm long, ripe in summer. **Flowering** in late winter and spring. **Habitat.** Common in woodlands, eucalypt forests and rainforest margins of the coast and tablelands in Qld and NSW. **Family.** Oleaceae.

Notelaea ligustrina   PRIVET MOCK OLIVE

A tall shrub or small tree, 2-10 m high, with a slender trunk and a dense bushy crown. **Mature leaves** are opposite, narrow lanceolate, thick, 4-15 cm long and 7-20 mm wide, dull dark green above and paler below with a prominent midrib and obscure lateral veins. **Flowers** are white to pale yellow, small and insignificant, cup-shaped with 4 lobes, arranged in axillary racemes to 3 cm long. **Fruits** are white, pink to dark purple or black fleshy ovoid drupes to 12 mm across, ripe in summer. **Flowering** in late winter and spring. **Habitat.** Sheltered rocky sites on slopes and near gullies in montane forests in NSW, Vic. and Tas. **Family.** Oleaceae.

Tasmannia lanceolata   MOUNTAIN PEPPER

A large shrub or small tree, 2-8 m high with a slender trunk and a much-branched rounded crown; the young stems are bright red. **Mature leaves** are alternate and clustered towards the ends of the branchlets, narrow lanceolate to narrow elliptic or oblanceolate, 3-13 cm long and 7-40 mm wide on very short stalks, dotted with oil glands, aromatic when crushed and with a peppery taste, glossy dark green above and paler below with a prominent midrib. **Flowers** are borne on separate male and female trees, they are creamy-white, open, about 1 cm across with 2-9 free curled back lobes about 1 cm long and 20-30 protruding stamens in males, arranged in terminal clusters on stalks 5-15 mm long. **Fruits** are shiny purple to black globular berries about 5 mm diameter. **Habitat.** Taller forests and woodlands on cool moist slopes and gullies in subalpine to lower montane areas in NSW, Vic. and Tas. **Family.** Winteraceae.

Notelaea longifolia

Notelaea ligustrina

Tasmannia lanceolata

M.Westmacott

Podocarpus elatus BROWN OR SHE PINE. ILLAWARRA PLUM

A large tree to 45 m high with an irregularly channeled, spirally fluted or flanged trunk to 1 m diameter and a compact, often conical crown. **Bark** is brown, fibrous and often finely fissured, with narrow vertical scales. **Mature leaves** are alternate, narrow-lanceolate to oblong or linear, sharply pointed, 4-18 cm long and 6-40 mm wide on stalks to 3 mm long, glossy dark green above and paler below with a prominent midrib. **Cones** are borne on separate male and female trees. Male cones are light brown, narrow cylindrical and catkin-like, 1-3 cm long, arranged in clusters of 2-10 in the leaf axils or above leaf scars. Female cones are small and inconspicuous before fertilisation, solitary, borne on stalks in the lower leaf axils or branchlets above leaf scars. They become fleshy and plum-like when mature, bluish-black or purplish, oblong, about 2 cm diameter on stalks to 25 mm long, with a resinous globular seed 8-12 mm diameter at the tip. They are ripe in autumn and winter. **Habitat.** Rainforests and scrub forests in coastal Qld and NSW. **Family.** Podocarpaceae.

Eremophila bignoniiflora BIGNONIA EMU BUSH. EURAH

A small tree to 7 m high with a dense rounded crown and pendulous branches. **Bark** is grey and rough; the branchlets are often pendulous and slightly sticky. **Mature leaves** are alternate, narrow lanceolate to linear, 3-18 cm long and 3-15 mm wide with a long pointed tip, thin, red tinged above and pale green below with a prominent midrib. **Flowers** are creamy white with purple spots, fragrant, tubular, 2-3 cm long, reddish outside, with 5 broad spreading lobes, the upper 2 may appear to be a notched lip and the lowest tongue-like, with 4 stamens. They are solitary or in small axillary clusters on sticky stalks 5-15 mm long. **Fruits** are ovoid fleshy drupes 15-20 mm long. **Flowering** in winter and spring. **Habitat.** Widespread inland on river flats and creek banks in open woodlands of all mainland states. **Family.** Myoporaceae.

Eremophila mitchellii BUDDA. FALSE SANDALWOOD

A tall shrub or small tree, 2-9 m high with a short trunk and rounded, medium-density crown of finely-textured .foliage. **Bark** is dark brown, hard, rough and closely fissured. **Mature leaves** are alternate, narrow lanceolate to linear, 3-7 cm long and 2-7 mm wide with a pointed hooked tip, thin, glossy dark green on both sides with a faint midrib. **Flowers** are white, cream or mauve, fragrant and bell-shaped, 12-20 mm long with 5 papery lobes, hairy inside with 4 stamens, solitary or in axillary pairs on sticky stalks 5-10 mm long. **Fruits** are ovoid fleshy drupes, 5-7 mm long, often 2-4 angled. **Flowering** most of the year. **Habitat.** Common in woodlands on the western slopes and plains, often on hillsides, in Qld and NSW. **Family.** Myoporaceae.

Podocarpus elatus

Erempohila bignoniiflora

Eremophila mitchellii

Acacia pycnantha   GOLDEN WATTLE

Australia's floral emblem, a tall shrub to small tree, 3-10 m high with a slender trunk, spreading branches and a rounded crown of pendulous foliage. **Bark** is dark brown and smooth, the branchlets are yellow-green and often angular with sharp ridges. **Mature leaves** (phyllodes) are alternate, narrow lanceolate to sickle-shaped or oblanceolate, glossy green and leathery with translucent margins and a small marginal gland within 1 cm of the base, 6-20 cm long and 1-5 cm wide with a prominent midrib. **Flowers** are packed into golden yellow fragrant fluffy balls, 8-10 mm diameter, arranged in slender racemes 8-15 cm long of 6-12 flowerheads, often forming a large drooping terminal panicle. **Fruits** are green turning brown linear to sickle-shaped flattish leathery pods, 5-13 cm long and 5-20 mm wide, slightly constricted between the 10-12 seeds. **Flowering** in late winter and spring. **Habitat.** Widespread in open forests in fairly low rainfall areas in southern NSW, northern Vic., eastern SA and WA. **Family.** Mimosaceae.

Acacia fimbriata   FRINGED WATTLE

A bushy shrub or small tree, 4-8 m high with a slender trunk and dense spreading crown of slightly drooping foliage. **Bark** is dark grey-brown, thin, slightly fibrous and flaky. **Mature leaves** (phyllodes) are alternate, narrow lanceolate to oblong, thin with minute hairs along the margins and a small gland near the base, 2-5 cm long and 2-5 mm wide, greyish-green with a prominent midrib. **Flowers** are packed into pale yellow fluffy balls about 5 mm diameter, arranged in long axillary racemes of 10-30 flowerheads. **Fruits** are bluish-brown flat straight pods, 5-7 cm long and about 7 mm wide, slightly constricted between the seeds, ripe in late spring. **Flowering** in late winter and spring. **Habitat.** Fairly common on a variety of soils except sandy sites, along riverbanks and in shady gullies of the coast and tablelands in southern Qld and NSW. **Family.** Mimosaceae.

Acacia longifolia   SYDNEY GOLDEN WATTLE

A bushy shrub or small tree, 2-10 m high with a variable form from a straight, slender tree in shaded bushland to a dense shrub with a low, widely-spreading crown. **Bark** is dull grey and smooth. **Mature leaves** (phyllodes) are alternate, narrow lanceolate to obovate with a small marginal gland near the base, 7-15 cm long and 10-35 mm wide, bright green with prominent longitudinal veins. **Flowers** are packed into golden yellow fluffy cylindrical spikes 2-6 cm long. **Fruits** are green turning pale brown narrow cylindrical leathery pods, 6-12 cm long and 3-8 mm wide, slightly constricted between the seeds, becoming curled and twisted when dry, ripe in late spring and early summer. **Flowering** in late winter and spring. **Habitat.** Widespread in forests, woodlands and cleared sites preferring moist sandy soils along the coast and tablelands in Qld, NSW, Vic., SA and Tas. **Family.** Mimosaceae.

Acacia pycnantha

Acacia fimbriata

Acacia longifolia

Geijera parviflora   WILGA

A tall shrub or small tree to 9 m high with a short stout trunk and a low broad rounded crown of dense pendulous foliage. **Bark** is dark grey to brown, rough and fissured. **Mature leaves** are alternate, narrow lanceolate to linear, pointed, 3-20 cm long and 3-8 mm wide, dull or glossy green with flattened stalks and many oil glands, aromatic when crushed. **Flowers** are white to cream, open, 4-5 mm across with 5 pointed lobes and 5 short stamens, arranged in loose terminal panicles 2-7 cm long. **Fruits** are greenish-brown globular capsules, 5-6 mm across, splitting open to reveal a single hard black shiny ovoid seed, about 4 mm across, ripe in spring and early summer. **Flowering** in winter and spring. **Habitat.** Mainly on red soil sandy loams inland in semi-arid areas of Qld, NSW, Vic. and SA. **Family.** Rutaceae.

Agonis flexuosa WILLOW MYRTLE. WESTERN AUSTRALIAN PEPPERMINT

A tall shrub to small tree, 2-15 m high, with a cylindrical trunk to 50 cm diameter and a fairly dense, rounded crown with drooping branchlets. **Bark** is grey or dark brown, rough, fibrous and furrowed. **Mature leaves** are alternate, narrow lanceolate to linear, aromatic, 5-15 cm long and 5-15 mm wide, reddish-brown when young, becoming shiny green with a prominent midrib and 2 distinct parallel veins near the margins. **Flowers** are white, open, about 1 cm across with 4-5 broad spreading lobes surrounding 16-20 short stamens, arranged in globular stalkless axillary heads of 8-14 flowers. **Fruits** are globular clusters of woody, flat-topped conical capsules each about 3-5 mm across forming a cluster about 1 cm across, containing small black seeds. **Flowering** in spring and early summer. **Habitat.** Moist sandy soils, sometimes in swampy sites in forests and woodlands along the coast in south-western WA, widely cultivated in temperate and tropical areas. **Family.** Myrtaceae.

Santalum acuminatum   QUANDONG. NATIVE PEAR

A tall shrub to small tree, 2-8 m high with a straight trunk, erect or spreading branches and a fairly sparse crown with pale green and often pendulous foliage. **Bark** is dark grey, rough and furrowed. **Mature leaves** are opposite, narrow lanceolate, sometimes sickle-shaped with a hooked tip, thick and leathery, 4-15 cm long and 4-12 mm wide, pale green with a prominent midrib. **Flowers** are creamy-white, small and tubular, 5-6 mm long with 4 slightly spreading lobes and 4 stamens, arranged in loose terminal panicles. **Fruits** are green turning red gobular edible drupes, 15-25 mm diameter with a light brown pitted stone containing an edible seed, ripe in summer. **Flowering** in spring and summer. **Habitat.** Widespread on light soils in low and moderate rainfall areas in woodlands and low-open forests inland in all mainland states. **Family.** Santalaceae.

Geijera parviflora

Agonis flexuosa

Santalum acuminatum

Oxylobium arborescens — TALL OXYLOBIUM

A tall shrub to small tree, 2-8 m high with a slender trunk and branchlets covered with soft hairs. **Mature leaves** are opposite, in whorls of 3-4 around the branchlets, narrow lanceolate to narrow ovate with a short sharp point and curved back margins, 2-8 cm long and 3-8 mm wide, dark green above with tiny protruding glands, paler below with silvery hairs and prominent midrib. **Flowers** are yellow, pea-shaped, 7-10 mm long with a broad notched standard petal, arranged in short terminal or axillary racemes. **Fruits** are densely hairy swollen ovoid pods, 6-10 mm long. **Flowering** in spring and early summer. **Habitat.** Locally common in open forests on shallow soils of the coast and tablelands in Qld, NSW, eastern Vic. and Tas. **Family.** Papilionaceae.

Pittosporum bicolor — BANYALLA

A tall shrub to small tree, 3-14 m high with a slender trunk and bushy crown. **Mature leaves** are alternate, narrow lanceolate to narrow elliptic with curled under margins, 2-8 cm long and 5-18 mm wide, leathery, dark green above and covered with silvery hairs below with a prominent midrib. **Flowers** are yellow and often crimson outside, tubular, about 1 cm long with 5 curled back lobes and 5 stamens, solitary or in small clusters in the leaf axils. **Fruits** are thick-walled ovoid orange capsules, downy outside, about 2 cm long and 5-10 mm across, opening to reveal numerous red seeds in a sticky pulp, ripe in autumn and winter. **Flowering** in spring. **Habitat.** Sheltered gullies in mountain forests below 1300 m, often beginning life as seedlings on tree fern trunks, in southeastern NSW, Vic. and Tas. **Family.** Pittosporaceae.

Pittosporum phillyreoides — WEEPING PITTOSPORUM. NATIVE APRICOT

A small tree to 14 m high with a cylindrical, sometimes longitudinally ridged trunk, long slender drooping branches and fairly open rounded crown. **Bark** is pale grey and smooth. **Mature leaves** are alternate, narrow lanceolate to linear with a small hooked pointed tip, 4-10 cm long and 3-10 mm wide on stalks about 5 mm long, thick, aromatic when crushed, with a prominent midrib. **Flowers** are pale yellow, tubular, scented, 6-9 mm long with 5 spreading to curled back lobes and 5 stamens, solitary or in small axillary clusters. **Fruits** are green turning orange, thick-walled, somewhat fleshy ovoid capsules, 1-2 cm long, splitting open to reveal several seeds in a sticky red pulp, ripe in autumn and winter. **Flowering** in winter and spring. **Habitat.** A common inland tree in mallee scrub and woodlands in low-lying areas along creek beds and sandy plains in all mainland states. **Family.** Pittosporaceae.

Oxylobium arborescens

Pittosporum bicolor

Pittosporum phillyreoides

Callistemon salignus — WILLOW OR WHITE BOTTLEBRUSH

A large shrub or small tree to 15 m high with a short, crooked, slender trunk and a bushy, straggly crown of medium density. **Bark** is light grey to white, papery and peeling in short strips in older trees. **Mature leaves** are alternate, narrow lanceolate, tapering at each end, 6-10 cm long and 7-15 mm wide on flattened stalks 3-4 mm long with a prominent midrib, soft, downy and reddish when young, becoming glossy darker green and more rigid when older, with numerous oil glands emitting an aromatic odour when crushed. **Flowers** are creamy-white, rarely pink, red or mauve, with 5 small lobes and numerous protruding stamens about 1 cm long, arranged in dense, hairy, cylindrical spikes, 3-8 cm long and 20-35 mm across often with leafy shoots growing from the tip. **Fruits** are hard woody almost globular capsules 3-5 mm across, stalkless and closely clustered around the branches for several years. **Flowering** in spring and early summer. **Habitat.** Widespread and common along stream banks and swamp edges of the coast and lower tablelands, extending to dry rocky montane sites in Qld and NSW. **Family.** Myrtaceae.

Melaleuca ericifolia — SWAMP PAPERBARK

A tall shrub to small tree, 2-9 m high with a bushy clumping low crown, slimmer and taller in shady sites. **Bark** is pale brown to grey, corky and peeling in long thin flakes, the branches are pale brown to whitish. **Mature leaves** are alternate or scattered and crowded along the branchlets, narrow lanceolate to linear, curved, 5-15 mm long and about 1 mm wide, dark green when older, without conspicuous veins. **Flowers** are creamy-white to yellow with 5 small lobes and numerous long protruding stamens fused at the bases into 5 bundles, arranged in short dense cylindrical spikes 2-7 cm long and 12-15 mm across, with new shoots often growing from the tips. **Fruits** are stalkless greyish-brown cylindrical to ovoid woody capsules about 3 mm diameter, closely clustered around the branchlets. **Flowering** in spring and early summer. **Habitat.** Coastal lagoons, swamps and stream flats, often forming closed scrub at lower elevations in southern Qld, NSW, Vic. and Tas. **Family.** Myrtaceae.

Melaleuca armillaris — GIANT OR BRACELET HONEY-MYRTLE

A large shrub to small tree, 2-14 m high with a short crooked trunk and broad rounded crown, often shrubby and congested in exposed sites. **Bark** is dark to light brown, corky and rough. **Mature leaves** are alternate, crowded on the branchlets, narrow lanceolate to linear with sharp, curved tips, often channelled above, 12-30 mm long and about 1 mm wide, dotted with oil glands and aromatic when crushed, with indistinct veins. **Flowers** are white to cream with 5 small lobes and numerous long protruding stamens fused at their bases into 5 bundles, arranged in dense cylindrical spikes 3-10 cm long and 2-3 cm across with new shoots often growing from the tips. **Fruits** are greyish-brown stalkless ovoid woody capsules, 3-5 mm across, closely clustered around the branchlets. **Flowering** in spring and summer. **Habitat.** Common in sandy heaths, cliffs and rocky outcrops along the coast of Qld, NSW, Vic. and Tas. **Family.** Myrtaceae.

Melaleuca ericifolia

Callistemon salignus

Melaleuca armillaris

Callistemon viminalis   DROOPING OR WEEPING BOTTLEBRUSH

A large shrub or small tree to 20 m high with a short, slender trunk, becoming spirally twisted in older trees, drooping branches and a dense, sometimes straggly crown. **Bark** is dark grey and rough with long vertical furrows twisting around the trunk in older trees; the young branches are covered with silky hairs. **Mature leaves** are alternate, narrow lanceolate, tapering at each end and held close to the branches, 2-7 cm long and 3-10 mm wide on very short stalks, with a prominent midrib, soft and downy with reddish tips when young, becoming darker green and more rigid when older, with numerous oil glands, emitting a myrtle scent when crushed. **Flowers** are bright red with 5 small lobes and numerous protruding stamens 18-22 mm long, arranged in dense, hairy, cylindrical terminal spikes, 4-20 cm long and 3-6 cm across often with leafy shoots growing from the tip. **Fruits** are hard woody cup-shaped capsules 5-6 mm across with 3 enclosed valves, clustered along the branches and shed annually. **Flowering** in spring and early summer. **Habitat.** Widespread and common along stream banks of the coast and tablelands in Qld and northeastern NSW. **Family.** Myrtaceae.

Angophora floribunda   ROUGH-BARKED APPLE

A medium-sized tree to 25 m high with a short trunk to 1 m diameter, often gnarled in older trees, spreading, twisting branches and an irregular large spreading open crown. **Bark** is pale brown, rough, thick, fibrous and fissured, and persistent to the small branches. **Mature leaves** are opposite, narrow lanceolate to oblong, 7-15 cm long and 10-35 mm wide, dull green above and paler below with conspicuous oil glands, young leaves are bright green. **Flowers** are creamy-white with numerous stamens to 1 cm long spreading from a short tubular calyx with a ribbed exterior and 5 small orbicular petals, arranged in dense terminal clusters on stalks with a few stiff hairs. **Fruits** are grey-brown soft, woody, cup-shaped capsules, 8-10 mm long and 8-12 mm across, with 5 main ribs and 3-4 enclosed valves with angular seeds to 4 mm long. **Flowering** in spring and summer. **Habitat.** Widespread in open forests or woodlands in deep soils of the lower slopes and coastal areas of Qld, NSW and Vic. **Family.** Myrtaceae.

Angophora costata   SMOOTH-BARKED APPLE. RED GUM

A medium-sized tree to 30 m high with a stout, straight trunk to 1.2 m diameter and an irregular, intricately branched large, open crown of red and green leaves. **Bark** is pink to orange-brown, turning grey before peeling, smooth and shed annually in thin scales leaving a slightly dimpled surface, often stained with exuding red kino. **Mature leaves** are opposite, narrow lanceolate, 7-16 cm long and 15-30 mm wide; young leaves are bright red becoming mid-green with a prominent yellowish midrib. **Flowers** are cream with numerous stamens to 1 cm long spreading from a short tubular calyx with a hairy, ribbed exterior and 5 short petals, arranged in dense terminal clusters on slightly hairy stalks. **Fruits** are grey-brown soft, woody, cup-shaped capsules, 13-15 mm long and 10-12 mm across, with 5 main ribs, a 5-toothed rim and 3-4 enclosed valves with large, flat seeds. **Flowering** in spring and summer. **Habitat.** Common on sandstone areas and coastal heaths in Qld, NSW and Vic. **Family.** Myrtaceae.

Callistemon viminalis

Angophora floribunda

Angophora costata

Xylomelum pyriforme
WOODY PEAR

A tall shrub to small tree, 3-11 m high with a slender cylindrical trunk. **Mature leaves** are opposite, whorled around the branchlets, narrow to broad lanceolate or ovate, 10-20 cm long and 3-4 cm wide on stalks 1-3 cm long, leathery, dark green above and paler below with coarse prominent veins; young leaves are soft rusty brown, often with prickly serrated margins. **Flowers** are yellowish-brown to creamy-white, covered with velvety brown hairs, tubular, 7-10 mm long with 4 curled back lobes and 4 stamens, arranged in dense axillary spikes 4-8 cm long forming a terminal cluster. **Fruits** are woody grey pear-shaped follicles, 5-15 cm long, splitting open when ripe to release 2 seeds each with a large brown wing. **Flowering** in late spring and summer. **Habitat.** Widespread in sandy soils in dry sclerophyll forests along the coast of Qld and NSW. **Family.** Proteaceae.

Agathis robusta
KAURI PINE. QUEENSLAND KAURI

A tall tree to 50 m high with a slightly tapering cylindrical trunk to 1.8 m diameter and a spreading crown with erect branches. **Bark** is brown to grey-brown, smooth to slightly flaky; young shoots are greyish. **Mature leaves** are opposite to slightly alternate or spirally arranged, lanceolate to elliptic, thick and leathery, 5-13 cm long and 1-4 cm wide on stalks 3-10 mm long, glossy dark green above and paler below with fine longitudinal veins. **Flowers** are separate male and female, borne on the same tree; males are brown cylindrical spikes to 10 cm long arising from the leaf axils; females are green globular cones. **Fruits** are ovoid brown woody cones 9-15 cm long and 8-10 cm wide on a thick stalk, with numerous scales each bearing a winged seed about 1 cm long. **Flowering** in spring. **Habitat.** Dry marginal rainforests, often forming stands, in eastern Qld. **Family.** Araucariaceae.

Araucaria bidwillii
BUNYA PINE

A tall tree to 50 m high with a long, straight, cylindrical trunk tapering slightly towards the top, to 1.5 m diameter, and a symmetrical dome-shaped crown with leaves clumped at the ends of straight, whorled, horizontal branches. **Bark** is dark brown to black, hard and rough with thin scales. **Mature leaves** are spirally arranged, stiff, narrow lanceolate, stalkless, 2-5 cm long and 5-10 mm wide, glossy green with a sharp point. **Flowers** are borne on short lateral branches, both male and female on the same tree; males are narrow cylindrical greenish-yellow spikes to 20 cm long made up of numerous spirally arranged scales covering the pollen cells; females are green, ovoid, about 12 mm diameter, composed of numerous sharply pointed scales. **Fruits** are large woody ovoid cones, dark green turning brown, 20-30 cm long and 10-20 cm across, composed of large scales each bearing a single flattened, pointed, egg-shaped seed 25-50 mm long with a milky edible flesh, ripe in autumn. **Flowering** in spring (males) and summer (females). **Habitat.** Favours rich volcanic soils in moist valleys, growing at various elevations and naturally occurring in rainforests of southeastern Qld and around Port Douglas in northeastern Qld, but widely cultivated in parks. **Family.** Araucariaceae.

Xylomelum pyriforme

Agathis robusta

Araucaria bidwillii

Persoonia linearis

NARROW-LEAF GEEBUNG

A tall shrub to small tree, 2-5 m high often with drooping branches. **Bark** is reddish or dark brown, loose and flaking, the branchlets are reddish and covered with soft white hairs. **Mature leaves** are alternate, often crowded along the branchlets, narrow lanceolate to linear, almost stalkless, 2-8 cm long and 2-4 mm wide, often with minute hairs. **Flowers** are yellow, tubular with a bulging base and covered with short soft hairs outside, about 12 mm long with 4 curled back lobes and 4 curled back protruding brown-striped stamens, solitary or in small axillary clusters along the terminal branchlets. **Fruits** are green fleshy globular drupes often with dark stripes, about 1 cm across. **Flowering** in summer. **Habitat.** Widespread and common on sandy and rocky soils in heaths and open forests along the coast and tablelands of Qld, NSW and Vic. **Family.** Proteaceae.

Persoonia levis

SMOOTH OR BROAD-LEAF GEEBUNG

A tall shrub to small tree, 2-5 m high with a short, slender trunk and a well-branched irregular crown. **Bark** is dark brown to black, loose and flaking, reddish on the branchlets. **Mature leaves** are alternate, lanceolate or oblanceolate, often sickle-shaped, 5-20 cm long and 1-4 cm wide on reddish stalks 4-10 mm long, bright green when young, becoming darker with 3 faint main veins. **Flowers** are yellow or cream, tubular with a bulging base, 10-12 mm long with 4 curled back lobes and 4 curled back protruding brown stamens, solitary or in small clusters along the branchlets on stalks 4-8 mm long. **Fruits** are green fleshy ovoid drupes to 15 mm long and 13 mm wide containing 1-2 seeds. **Flowering** in summer. **Habitat.** Common on sandy soils in heaths and dry sclerophyll forests along the coast and lower tablelands of NSW and Vic. **Family.** Proteaceae.

Tristaniopsis laurina (syn. Tristania laurina)

WATERGUM. KANUKA

A small to medium-sized tree, 5-27 m high with an irregular or channelled trunk to 75 cm diameter and a dense, dark green, spreading crown. **Bark** is light grey to pale brown, smooth and shedding in thin papery ribbons. **Mature leaves** are alternate and clustered at the ends of the branchlets, narrow lanceolate to narrow elliptic, often broader in the upper half of the leaf, 5-14 cm long and 1-3 cm wide on channelled stalks 6-10 mm long, glossy dark green above and paler below with numerous small oil glands and a conspicuous midrib raised below with lateral veins visible above. **Flowers** are yellow with a bell-shaped calyx and 5 widely separated oval lobes around the rim, about 1 cm across with numerous stamens united into 5 bundles at the base, arranged in small axillary clusters. **Fruits** are oval, domed capsules about 1 cm long splitting open at the top into 3 valves each with numerous flattened seeds about 6 mm long, ripe in early winter. **Flowering** in summer. **Habitat.** Common along watercourses, sometimes in or near rainforests, especially near coastal dunes, along the coast and lower tablelands in Qld, NSW and Vic. **Family.** Myrtaceae.

Persoonia linearis

Persoonia levis

Tristaniopsis laurina

Banksia occidentalis   RED SWAMP BANKSIA. WATERBUSH

A large shrub or small tree, 3-8 m high with a slender trunk and dense crown. **Bark** is brown-grey and smooth, younger branches are bright red and sometimes slightly hairy. **Mature leaves** are whorled regularly around the branches, narrow lanceolate to linear with notched tips and curved back margins, 5-15 cm long and 2-3 mm wide, green above and whitish below with a prominent midrib. **Flowers** are ruby red and yellow, tubular with long, red, wiry, hooked, protruding styles when released, arranged in cylindrical upright spikes, 10-15 cm long and 6-10 cm diameter on short axillary stalks. **Fruits** are woody cylindrical cones retaining the dead flowers for a long time, about 10-15 cm long and 6-10 cm diameter with numerous brown protruding follicles containing 2 flat winged seeds. **Flowering** in summer and early autumn. Habitat. Common in swampy sites near the south coast of WA from Denmark to Esperance. **Family.** Proteaceae.

Banksia ericifolia   HEATH BANKSIA

A large shrub or small tree, 2-7 m high with a short slender trunk and compact crown, often with branches near ground level. **Bark** is grey-brown, smooth and scaly with small rough patches on the main trunk and larger branches. **Mature leaves** are crowded, narrow lanceolate to linear with notched tips, 1-2 cm long and 2-3 mm wide, dark green above and silvery below with curved back margins. **Flowers** are orange-red, small and tubular with long, wiry, hooked, protruding styles when released, arranged in cylindrical upright spikes, 10-30 cm long and 4-6 cm diameter. **Fruits** are long and narrow woody cylindrical cones with numerous brown protruding follicles containing usually 2 flat winged seeds, retained after maturity. **Flowering** in winter and spring **Habitat.** Widespread and common on sandy soils of coastal heaths and scrubs in NSW. **Family.** Proteaceae.

Banksia integrifolia   COAST BANKSIA

A medium sized tree to 20 m high and about 50 cm diameter, but usually under 10 m high and gnarled and twisted or straggling along the coast, stunted and shrubby in exposed sites; young branches are covered in white downy hairs. **Bark** is hard, rough, light grey, sometimes fissured, with a granular appearance, persistent on the trunk and main limbs. **Mature leaves** are in whorls of 4-6, becoming alternate when older, oblong to narrow lanceolate or wedge-shaped with a short stalk, sometimes with shortly-toothed margins, 4-15 cm long and 1-7 cm wide, dark green above and covered with silvery white hairs below, with a prominent midrib, net-like veins and often with curved back margins. **Flowers** are pale yellow, small and tubular with long, wiry, straight, protruding styles, arranged in cylindrical terminal upright spikes, 5-15 cm long and 5-8 cm diameter. **Fruits** are grey cylindrical cones about 7-15 cm long and 7-8 cm diameter with numerous brown protruding follicles containing usually 2 black winged ovate seeds, released on maturity. **Flowering** most of the year. **Habitat.** Widespread on poor soils along the coast and adjacent tablelands in Qld, NSW, Vic. and Tas. **Family.** Proteaceae.

Banksia occidentalis

Banksia ericifolia

Banksia integrifolia

Choricarpia leptopetala (syn. Syncarpia l.) BRUSH TURPENTINE

A small to medium-sized tree to 20 m high with a short, often crooked trunk to about 25 cm diameter, slightly flanged at the base in older trees, and a bushy crown with dense heads of creamy-white flowers. **Bark** is brown or greyish-brown, corky, often with vertical fissures. **Mature leaves** are opposite, broad lanceolate to ovate, sometimes with a fine point and curved back margins, 5-13 cm long and 2-4 cm wide on leaf stalks 3-10 mm long, glossy dark green above and greyish-green below, producing a pleasant fragrance when crushed. Veins are sunken above and more prominent below with an indistinct vein close to the margin. **Flowers** are white or cream, small and tubular, 2-3 mm long with numerous protruding stamens, in dense globular heads 15-20 mm across on slender stalks 1-4 cm long. They are terminal or axillary with 2-3 heads together. **Fruits** are dark brown small conical hairy capsules, about 2 mm across, crowded into globular heads about 13 mm diameter, ripe in winter, persistent for several months. **Flowering** in spring and summer. **Habitat.** Rainforest margins along creek banks and ridges in moist eucalypt forests on poorer soils in southeastern Qld and NSW. **Family.** Myrtaceae.

Hakea salicifolia WILLOW-LEAVED HAKEA

A tall shrub or small tree, 2-8 m high with an erect, slender, short trunk, many branches and a dense bushy crown. **Bark** is pale greenish-brown becoming reddish-brown. **Mature leaves** are alternate, broad to narrow lanceolate with a sharply pointed tip, 5-15 cm long and 10-25 mm wide on a stalk 4-5 mm long, reddish with silky hairs when young, becoming shiny grey-green above and paler below with a prominent midrib. **Flowers** are white, tubular, 4-5 mm long with 4 narrow curved back lobes and a long, curved, protruding style when released, arranged in short dense axillary clusters of 10-20 flowers. **Fruits** are grey-brown globular warty woody follicles, 1-3 cm long and about 15 mm wide with a short 2-pronged beak, splitting into 2 segments each with a broad winged seed. **Flowering** in spring. **Habitat.** Widespread in tall forests, woodlands, rainforest margins and scrubs in wet gullies and near streams along the coast and lower slopes in Qld and NSW. **Family.** Proteaceae.

Capparis mitchellii WILD ORANGE

A tall shrub or small tree, 3-10 m high often with several joined main stems forming a wide short trunk in older trees, and many spreading branches giving a wide dense low crown. **Bark** is dark brown to black and deeply fissured, young branches are spiny and clothed with dense woolly hairs. **Mature leaves** are alternate, broad lanceolate to elliptic or ovate, thick and stiff, 20-65 mm long and 1-3 cm wide on thick stalks 5-10 mm long, covered in dense woolly hairs with prominent veins below. **Flowers** are white, cream or yellow, open, 5-6 cm across with broad lobes and numerous very long protruding stamens, solitary or in terminal or axillary clusters of 2-4 flowers on thick stalks 2-4 cm long. **Fruits** are green rough globular berries, 4-7 cm across containing large flat seeds, turning dark orange to purple-black when ripe. **Flowering** most of the year. **Habitat.** Widespread in arid inland forests, grasslands and woodlands of NT, Qld, NSW and SA. **Family.** Capparidaceae.

Choricarpia leptopetala

Hakea salicifolia

Capparis mitchellii

Hakea laurina   PINCUSHION HAKEA

A tall shrub or small tree, 3-8 m high with an erect, slender, short trunk, slightly pendulous outer branches and a dense low rounded crown. **Bark** is reddish-brown, the young branchlets are covered with silky golden-brown hairs. **Mature leaves** are alternate, broad lanceolate with a sharply pointed curved tip, 8-18 cm long and 10-25 mm wide, thick and leathery, dull blue-green with 3 main longitudinal veins. **Flowers** are bright red with protruding cream styles, producing a globular pincushion-like flowerhead 4-6 cm diameter, consisting of numerous tubular flowers each with 4 narrow, red, curved back lobes and a long, straight, protruding cream style; the flowerheads are solitary in the upper leaf axils. **Fruits** are grey-brown globular, warty, woody follicles 2-3 cm long with a short, curved beak, splitting into 2 segments each with a broad winged seed. **Flowering** in autumn and winter. **Habitat.** Sheltered sunny slopes of the southwestern coast of WA, but widely cultivated. **Family.** Proteaceae.

Telopea oreades   TREE OR GIPPSLAND WARATAH

A tall shrub or small tree to 14 m high with a slender trunk to 50 cm diameter and a dense rounded crown of dark green foliage. **Bark** is dark brown, thin and smooth. **Mature leaves** are alternate, whorled around the stems, broad lanceolate to narrow obovate often with curved back margins, rarely with a few small teeth near the tip, 8-25 cm long and 2-5 cm wide, dull dark green above, paler below with a prominent midrib. **Flowers** are deep crimson, tubular, slit on one side with 4 curled back lobes and a long protruding style, arranged in dense, terminal, globular heads 7-10 cm diameter. **Fruits** are leathery curved follicles, 5-8 cm long, opening longitudinally to release numerous winged seeds. **Flowering** in summer. **Habitat.** Well-drained sheltered sites, often along streams in cool moist gullies and montane forests to 1300 m in the coastal ranges of NSW and Vic. **Family.** Proteaceae.

Oreocallis pinnata (syn. O. wickhamii) RED SILKY OAK. TREE WARATAH

A small to medium-sized tree, 8-30 m high with a short cylindrical trunk to 1 m or more diameter and a dense low ovoid crown in the open, but taller with a higher tufted crown in the bush. **Bark** is grey-brown with a sandpapery texture and small blisters, deep red when cut; new growth is rusty-hairy and the branchlets are chocolate brown. **Mature leaves** are alternate, very variable from broad lanceolate to linear, sometimes lobed near the tip, 10-30 cm long and 1-5 cm wide on rusty-hairy slender ridged stalks 12-25 mm long, swollen at the base, glossy dark green above and paler below with prominent veins. **Flowers** are bright orange-crimson, tubular, 2-5 cm long on slender stalks 25-40 mm long, split along one side with a long curved style, arranged in dense terminal or axillary spikes 5-7 cm long. **Fruits** are brown woody oblong follicles, 8-10 cm long, splitting along one side to release closely packed flat winged seeds, ripe in autumn and winter. **Flowering** in late spring and early summer. **Habitat.** Common in highland rainforests and their fringes along the coast of Qld and northern NSW. **Family.** Proteaceae.

Hakea laurina

Telopea oreades

Oreocallis pinnata

Pittosporum revolutum   ROUGH-FRUIT PITTOSPORUM

A bushy shrub to small tree, 2-6 m high with a slender trunk and a dense, compact, rounded crown. **Bark** is dark brown and smooth, the young branchlets are covered in dense rusty hairs. **Mature leaves** are alternate, occasionally whorled at the ends of the branchlets in groups of 4-8, broad lanceolate to ovate or elliptic, often with wavy curled back margins, 4-13 cm long and 2-6 cm wide on stalks 1-2 cm long, leathery, glossy dark green above and covered with rusty hairs below with a prominent midrib. **Flowers** are creamy-yellow, slightly fragrant, tubular, about 15 mm long with 5 curled back lobes and 5 stamens, arranged in terminal clusters. **Fruits** are hard, thick-walled orange ovoid capsules, 20-25 mm long, splitting open into 2 sections to reveal numerous reddish-brown seeds in a sticky pulp, ripe in late summer and autumn. **Flowering** in spring. **Habitat.** Widespread in forests on sheltered sites along the coast of southeastern Qld, NSW and eastern Vic. **Family.** Pittosporaceae.

Glochidion ferdinandi (syn. Phyllanthus ferdinandi)   CHEESE TREE

A tall shrub or small tree to 12 m high with a crooked and often flanged trunk to 40 cm diameter and a dense, spreading crown. **Bark** is purplish-brown to grey-brown, fissured and falling in longitudinal patches; it is light brown and smooth on the slender branchlets. **Mature leaves** are alternate and arranged in 2 rows to give a pinnate appearance, broad lanceolate to elliptic, 5-9 cm long and 2-4 cm wide on leaf stalks 3-5 mm long, shiny green above and sometimes downy below, with the midrib raised on both surfaces. **Flowers** are small and inconspicuous, greenish-yellow, about 3 mm long, male and female flowers are separate on the same tree, the males are often clustered in threes with 6 lobes and 3 stamens, the females are solitary in the leaf axils. **Fruits** are green to pinkish capsules turning red, globular and flattened with 5-7 cells furrowed between them to give a pumpkin-like appearance, 1-2 cm across, opening to expose 4-6 pairs of flattened seeds 4-5 mm diameter and covered by a red skin, ripe in summer. **Flowering** mainly in spring. **Habitat.** Common in sheltered gullies, on river banks, near swamps and in rainforest margins in Qld, NSW, northwestern WA and NT. **Family.** Euphorbiaceae.

Alphitonia excelsa   RED ASH

A small to medium-sized tree to 35 m high with a straight trunk to 1.25 m diameter and a medium density crown, high in rainforest habitats, but low and spreading in open sites, with conspicuous silvery leaves below. **Bark** is steel-grey, hard, rough and deeply fissured longitudinally, with a pinkish inner bark and white sapwood. **Mature leaves** are alternate, broad lanceolate to elliptic with a sharp point, 7-15 cm long and 1-4 cm wide on leaf stalks 1-2 cm long, glossy dark green above and covered with silvery hairs below; new growth is covered with grey or rusty down. Veins are sunken above and more prominent below with 13-18 main lateral veins. **Flowers** are greenish-cream, open, fragrant, 2-6 mm across with 5 small hood-shaped petals each enclosing one stamen, arranged in terminal or axillary panicles. **Fruits** are green turning black, globular, thinly succulent drupes, 5-10 mm diameter, containing 2 hard cells each with a glossy dark brown seed covered by a thin dark orange skin, ripe in spring and early summer. **Flowering** in summer and early autumn. **Habitat.** Widespread in open eucalypt forests and adjoining rainforests along the coast, lower tablelands and western slopes in NT, Qld, NSW and WA. **Family.** Rhamnaceae.

Pittosporum revolutum

Glochidion ferdinandi

Alphitonia excelsa

Melaleuca quinquenervia   BROAD-LEAVED PAPERBARK
A small or occasionally medium-sized tree, 4-25 m high with a slender trunk, few
branches and compact crown. **Bark** is white to light brown, thick, spongy and
rough, peeling readily in large sheets. **Mature leaves** are alternate, broad lanceolate
to oblanceolate, 4-15 cm long and 15-30 mm wide on flat twisted stalks 5-6 mm
long, dark green with 5 conspicuous longitudinal veins. **Flowers** are white to cream
with 5 small lobes and numerous long protruding stamens fused at their bases into
5 clawed bundles, arranged in dense cylindrical spikes, 4-8 cm long and 25-35 mm
across with new shoots often growing from the tip. **Fruits** are woody cup-shaped
grey-brown stalkless capsules about 5 mm across, clustered around the branchlets
where they persist for up to a year. **Flowering** in autumn and winter. **Habitat.**
Common along stream banks and swamp margins in low woodlands and heaths
along the coast north from Sydney in NSW to northern Qld. **Family.** Myrtaceae.

Melaleuca styphelioides   PRICKLY-LEAVED PAPERBARK
A small or occasionally medium-sized tree, 4-25 m high with a slender trunk and a
dense rounded crown with slightly drooping branchlets. **Bark** is white to light
brown, spongy and peeling in large flakes. **Mature leaves** are alternate, crowded
along the branchlets, broad lanceolate to narrow ovate with a sharp point and
twisted, 1-2 cm long and 3-5 mm wide on very short stalks, bright green maturing
to dark green with many fine parallel veins. **Flowers** are cream and white with 5
small lobes and numerous long protruding stamens fused at their bases into 5
clawed bundles, arranged in dense cylindrical spikes 2-5 cm long and 1-2 cm across
with new shoots often growing from the tip. **Fruits** are grey-brown woody ovoid
stalkless capsules, 3-4 mm across, closely clustered around the branchlets.
Flowering in summer. **Habitat.** Creek banks and moist, heavy soils of the coast and
lower tablelands in central and northern NSW, widely planted in streets and parks.
Family. Myrtaceae.

Melaleuca leucadendron   LONG-LEAVED PAPERBARK
A tall tree to 43 m high with a straight trunk to 1 m diameter and a high compact
crown with pendulous branchlets. **Bark** is white, smooth and often blotched with
brownish older bark, papery, layered and slightly peeling. **Mature leaves** are
alternate, broad lanceolate, rigid, 8-20 cm long and 1-4 cm wide, light green with 3
prominent longitudinal veins. **Flowers** are cream to white with 5 small lobes and
numerous long protruding stamens fused at their bases into 5 bundles, arranged in
cylindrical spikes 6-20 cm long and 2-3 cm across with new shoots often growing
from the tip. **Fruits** are grey-brown woody cup-shaped stalkless capsules, 3-4 mm
across, closely clustered around the branchlets. **Flowering** in spring. **Habitat.**
Swamps, lagoons and river flats, often in open forests in northeastern Qld, northern
NT to northwestern WA. **Family.** Myrtaceae.

Melaleuca quinquenervia

Melaleuca styphelioides

Melaleuca leucadendron

Leptospermum lanigerum   WOOLLY TEA TREE

A tall shrub or small tree, 2-6 m high with a dense, erect crown of greyish-green foliage and hairy branchlets. **Bark** is grey, papery, corky and somewhat stringy. **Mature leaves** are alternate, broad lanceolate to oblong, often convex above, with a sharp point, 5-25 mm long and 2-4 mm wide on very short silky hairy stalks, dull grey-green above and paler below with silvery hairs. **Flowers** are white, open, 1-2 cm across with 5 separate spreading lobes around a green central disc surrounded by numerous stamens and 5 red sepals, with a short densely-woolly calyx tube, stalkless and solitary or in small axillary clusters. **Fruits** are domed woody capsules with a depressed centre, 7-12 mm across with 5 valves opening to release very slender seeds. **Flowering** in spring and early summer. **Habitat.** Widespread in moist sandy sites, usually at lower elevations in Qld, NSW, Vic., SA and Tas. **Family.** Myrtaceae.

Eupomatia laurina   BOLWARRA. COPPER LAUREL. NATIVE GUAVA

A shrub or small bushy tree, 3-15 m high with a crooked trunk to 30 cm diameter, weak branches and a dense crown. **Bark** is brown, slightly corky or scaly with fine vertical fissures. **Mature leaves** are alternate, broad lanceolate to elliptic, 5-16 cm long and 2-5 cm wide on stalks about 3 mm long with a short point at the tip, waxy, glossy green, sometimes coppery, paler below. **Flowers** are cream and waxy with a strong fragrance, the petals and sepals form a cap that is shed as the flower opens leaving numerous petal-like stamens 5-10 mm long which give the flower a daisy-like appearance. They are 20-25 mm across on stalks 5-7 mm long, solitary, arising from the leaf axils or the scars of fallen leaves. **Fruits** are green, succulent, edible, urn-shaped with a flat top, 15-20 mm across and containing numerous achenes, ripe in autumn and winter. **Flowering** in spring and summer. **Habitat.** Widespread in rainforests and wet sclerophyll forests near shaded streams of the coast and adjacent plateaux in Qld, NSW and Vic. **Family.** Eupomatiaceae.

Pittosporum undulatum   SWEET PITTOSPORUM. MOCK ORANGE

A small to medium-sized tree, 4-30 m high with a crooked and often flanged trunk in large trees to 35 cm diameter, and a dense, rounded crown. **Bark** is dark brownish-grey, rough and scaly in older trees; the branches exude a sticky resin. **Mature leaves** are alternate but crowded in groups of 3-6 towards the ends of the branchlets, lanceolate with wavy margins, 6-15 cm long and 2-5 cm wide on stalks 1-2 cm long, tapering to a fine sharp point, glossy green above and paler below. **Flowers** are white, fragrant, bell-shaped, about 9 mm long with 5 spreading, rounded lobes and 5 stamens, arranged in terminal clusters. **Fruits** are yellow turning orange globular fleshy capsules with a short fine point at the tip, 8-15 mm across, splitting open in 2 parts to reveal numerous brown or orange angular seeds 1-3 mm long with a viscous covering, ripe in autumn and winter. **Flowering** in spring. **Habitat.** Rainforests, scrubby gullies, rocky mountainsides in open forests of the coast and tablelands in southern Qld, NSW, Vic., SA and Tas. **Family.** Pittosporaceae.

Leptospermum lanigerum

Eupomatia laurina

Pittosporum undulatum

Acacia melanoxylon   BLACKWOOD

A medium-sized to tall tree, 15-30 m high with a fairly cylindrical trunk to 90 cm diameter, sometimes shortly buttressed or flanged at the base, and a dense bushy crown with angular branchlets. **Bark** is grey-brown, hard, scaly and fissured, and shedding in narrow vertical strips. **Mature leaves** (phyllodes) are alternate, broad lanceolate to sickle-shaped, 6-15 cm long and 6-30 mm wide, thick, with usually 3-5 longitudinal main veins. **Flowers** are pale yellow and crowded into fluffy globular heads about 1 cm across on short stalks, solitary or a few together in short axillary racemes 25-50 mm long. **Fruits** are pale brown flatish pods becoming twisted or coiled when ripe, 4-12 cm long and about 8 mm wide with black oval seeds connected to the pod by a long red thread twice encircling the seed, ripe in summer. **Flowering** in winter and spring. **Habitat.** Common on a variety of sites with rainfall exceeding 600 mm, particularly on deep soils in tall forests and rainforests of the coast and tablelands in Qld, NSW, Vic., SA and Tas. **Family.** Mimosaceae.

Bedfordia arborescens (syn. B. salicina)   BLANKET LEAF

A small tree to 12 m high with a short crooked trunk to 45 cm diameter and a spreading rounded crown with low branches and terminal clusters of long dark green leaves. **Bark** is grey to greyish-brown, rough, deeply fissured or scaly; the branchlets are clothed with long white tangled hairs. **Mature leaves** are alternate, radiating around the end of the branchlets, broad lanceolate to oblong with wavy margins, 15-24 cm long and 20-45 mm wide on stalks 15-20 mm long, dark green above and covered with long white matted hairs below, with a prominent midrib and lateral veins visible above. **Flowers** are bright yellow and clustered into composite tubular flowerheads 6-10 mm long, comprising 15-20 tubular flowers enclosed in 8 pointed woolly bracts 5-6 mm long, arranged in long woolly axillary panicles. **Fruits** are small ribbed cigar-shaped achenes, 2-4 mm long, crowned with a ring of silver bristles to 8 mm long, ripe in summer. **Flowering** in spring and summer. **Habitat.** Widespread and common in cool sheltered forests and rainforests in mountain sites in NSW, Vic. and SA. **Family.** Compositae.

Acacia prominens   GOLDEN RAIN OR GOSFORD WATTLE

A tall shrub to medium-sized tree, 5-25 m high with a straight short trunk, well-branched with a fine, low dense crown. **Bark** is smooth and grey. **Mature leaves** (phyllodes) are broad lanceolate to narrow elliptic, slightly sickle-shaped, 2-6 cm long and 5-10 mm wide with a small protruding marginal gland, light blue-green with a silvery bloom and prominent midrib. **Flowers** are pale yellow, sweetly perfumed and crowded into fluffy globular heads about 8 mm across on short stalks, arranged in dense slender axillary racemes 3-7 cm long. **Fruits** are bluish green flat straight pods, 3-8 cm long. **Flowering** in early spring. **Habitat.** Forests and rainforest margins along creeks of the coast and adjacent plateaux in central NSW, but widely cultivated. **Family.** Mimosaceae.

Acacia melanoxylon

Bedfordia arborescens

M. Westmacott

Acacia prominens

Syzygium paniculatum (syn. Eugenia paniculata) BRUSH CHERRY

A small tree to 18 m high with a short, irregular and often slightly buttressed trunk to 35 cm diameter and a dense crown with low branches. **Bark** is brown, soft and scaly, sometimes with fine fissures. **Mature leaves** are opposite in pairs, lanceolate to elliptic, 3-8 cm long and 1-3 cm wide on slender stalks 2-10 mm long, glossy dark green above and paler below with indistinct scattered oil dots and raised midrib below. The young leaves and stems are reddish, and the young stems 4-angled. **Flowers** are creamy-white with a funnel-shaped calyx crowned with 4 rounded lobes 4-6 mm long and numerous long, protruding stamens, arranged in small terminal or axillary panicles of 1-3 flowers on short stalks. **Fruits** are dark red to pinkish-red glossy oval to pear-shaped berries, 12-25 mm long, containing a single rounded seed inside an edible, crisp and slightly acidic pulp, ripe in autumn and winter. **Flowering** mainly in summer and autumn. **Habitat.** Very common on sandy soils in beach rainforests and near freshwater streams in or near other rainforest types to 1000 m along the coast of Qld, NSW and NT. **Family.** Myrtaceae.

Syzygium crebrinerve (syn. Eugenia crebrinervis) PURPLE CHERRY

A large tree to 40 m high with an irregular and prominently buttressed trunk in large trees, to 90 cm diameter, and a dark green shiny crown with bright red new growth. **Bark** is pale grey-brown, smooth or slightly flaky with longitudinal fissures and numerous depressions. **Mature leaves** are opposite, lanceolate to narrow elliptic with curled under margins and a long tapering point, 5-15 cm long and 1-7 cm wide on stalks 6-16 mm long, glossy dark green above and paler below with a raised midrib, fine lateral veins and numerous regularly spaced oil glands giving an aromatic odour when crushed, drying to red-brown. **Flowers** are white with a funnel-shaped calyx about 6 mm long, crowned with 4 rounded lobes 2-5 mm long and numerous long, protruding stamens, arranged in small terminal or axillary panicles. **Fruits** are dark red to purple globular, slightly flattened berries, 13-25 mm across, containing a single irregularly shaped seed, concave below and rounded above with a short point, about 5 mm across, inside a dry, mealy and slightly acidic pulp, ripe in summer. **Flowering** in late spring. **Habitat.** Common in subtropical rainforests on plateaux and coastal ranges of Qld and NSW. **Family.** Myrtaceae.

Syzygium luehmannii (syn. Eugenia l.) SMALL-LEAVED WATERGUM

A medium-sized tree to 30 m high with a straight trunk usually buttressed in large trees, to 90 cm diameter, and a dense crown of small leaves with bright pink soft new growth and slender branchlets. **Bark** is grey to reddish-brown, smooth or slightly flaky with irregular shallow depressions. **Mature leaves** are opposite, lanceolate to ovate with a long tapering point, 3-7 cm long and 10-25 mm wide on stalks 2-4 mm long, glossy dark green above and paler below with a raised midrib and numerous conspicuous oil glands, giving an aromatic odour when crushed. **Flowers** are white with a funnel-shaped calyx crowned with 4-5 rounded lobes about 2 mm long, and numerous protruding stamens about 5 mm long, arranged in small axillary or terminal panicles. **Fruits** are red pear-shaped berries 9-13 mm long, containing a single seed about 4 mm diameter surrounded by a white mealy pulp, ripe in summer. **Flowering** in late spring. **Habitat.** Common in rainforests and scrublands in sandy soils along the coast of Qld and northern NSW. **Family.** Myrtaceae.

Syzygium paniculatum

Syzygium crebrinerve

Syzygium luehmannii

Archirhodomyrtus beckleri (syn. Rhodomyrtus beckleri)   ROSE MYRTLE

A tall shrub or small tree, 4-15 m high with a slender angular trunk to 25 cm diameter and a bushy crown. **Bark** is light brown, fibrous and flaky with narrow longitudinal lines. **Mature leaves** are opposite, broad lanceolate to ovate with a strong aromatic odour when crushed, 2-8 cm long and 7-25 mm wide on stalks 2-6 mm long, thick, glossy green above and paler below with a prominent midrib and 2 prominent longitudinal veins. **Flowers** are mauve to pink or white, open, about 1 cm across with 5 curled back lobes and numerous protruding stamens, solitary or with 2-3 flowers on an axillary stalk 5-25 mm long. **Fruits** are yellow, turning orange or red, globular berries 5-8 mm diameter containing numerous seeds in 3 cells, ripe in summer. **Flowering** in spring. **Habitat.** Widespread in open forests and rainforests, especially in cleared areas, generally on poorer soils along the coast and adjacent ranges in Qld and NSW. **Family.** Myrtaceae.

Waterhousea floribunda (syn. Syzygium f.)   WEEPING LILLY PILLY

A large tree to 30 m high, usually smaller in the open, with a thick trunk to 75 cm diameter, often slightly flanged at the base in large trees, and a low broad dense crown of pendulous branchlets and dark green leaves. **Bark** is grey to dark grey-brown, fissured and deeply furrowed in large trees, often with some detached narrow scales. **Mature leaves** are opposite, broad lanceolate to narrow elliptic with a fine point and wavy margins, 5-16 cm long and 15-50 mm wide on slender channelled stalks 3-8 mm long, thin and soft, dark glossy green above and paler below with a raised midrib, aromatic when crushed. **Flowers** are white or yellow, 7-12 mm diameter with a funnel-shaped calyx crowned with 4 rounded lobes and numerous long protruding stamens, arranged in small terminal or axillary panicles on stalks 1-3 mm long. **Fruits** are greenish turning dull white globular berries, 13-20 mm diameter, with a large single seed covered by a fleshy skin, ripe in spring. **Flowering** in late spring and summer. **Habitat.** Gullies, river flats and rainforests, generally alongside waterways along the coast of central and northern NSW and Qld. **Family.** Myrtaceae.

Mallotus philippensis   RED KAMALA

A small to medium-sized tree, 8-25 m high with a short cylindrical trunk to 40 cm diameter, often fluted and flanged at the base in large trees, with a bushy crown. **Bark** is grey, smooth or wrinkled with scattered corky blisters, deep red when cut; the branchlets are often covered with rusty down towards the ends. **Mature leaves** are alternate, broad lanceolate to ovate, 5-13 cm long and 2-5 cm wide on rusty brown stalks 2-5 cm long, glossy green above and paler with greyish down below, the midrib is raised below and 2 prominent veins originate at the base of the leaf, running parallel to the margin for over half its length. **Flowers** are yellow-brown, very small, arranged in rusty-hairy terminal or axillary racemes to 6 cm long on separate male and female trees. **Fruits** are globular capsules usually with 3 lobes, 6-9 mm across, covered with a deep red powdery substance, with a single globular seed in each cell, ripe in spring and summer. **Flowering** in winter and spring. **Habitat.** Common in open country, rainforests and forest margins usually near watercourses along the coast of central and northern NSW and Qld. **Family.** Euphorbiaceae.

Archirhodomyrtus beckleri

Waterhousea floribunda

Mallotus philippensis

Backhousia myrtifolia   GREY MYRTLE. IRONWOOD

A tall shrub or small tree, 3-12 m high with a cylindrical trunk often slightly flanged or buttressed at the base in large trees, and a dense low spreading crown. **Bark** is brown and scaly with vertical fissures. **Mature leaves** are opposite, ovate to elliptic with a long fine point and numerous small oil glands, 3-7 cm long and 10-35 mm wide on stalks 2-6 mm long, dark green above and paler with a raised midrib and conspicuous veins below. **Flowers** are pale yellow-green, open, 15-20 mm across with 5 pointed lobes and numerous protruding stamens about 6 mm long, the calyx tube is covered with soft white hairs, and they are arranged in small, terminal or axillary leafy clusters. **Fruits** are dry capsules enclosed in the hairy bell-shaped calyx, about 1 cm long, ripe in autumn. **Flowering** in summer. **Habitat.** Common in damp gullies and closed forests, rainforests and rainforest margins along the coast and adjacent tablelands of Qld and NSW. **Family.** Myrtaceae.

Melaleuca squarrosa   SCENTED PAPERBARK

A tall shrub to small tree, 2-10 m high with a spreading crown. **Bark** is pale grey, corky and peeling in thin strips. **Mature leaves** are opposite in pairs at right angles, crowded, ovate to broad lanceolate, 5-18 mm long and 3-7 mm wide on very short stalks, stiff and dark green with 5 indistinct main veins. **Flowers** are cream to yellow, scented, with 5 small lobes and numerous long protruding stamens fused at their bases into 5 bundles, arranged in cylindrical spikes 15-50 mm long and 1-2 cm wide with new shoots often growing from the tips. **Fruits** are pale brown woody ovoid stalkless capsules, 3-5 mm across, closely clustered around the branchlets. **Flowering** in spring and summer. **Habitat.** Often forms closed scrub on peaty sands near swamps and streams along the coast of central and southern NSW, Vic., SA and Tas. **Family.** Myrtaceae.

Syncarpia glomulifera   RED TURPENTINE

A tall tree to 60 m high with a long cylindrical trunk to 1.5 m diameter and a bushy, fairly compact crown. **Bark** is dark brown or reddish, thick, flaky and fibrous with deep longitudinal furrows. **Mature leaves** are opposite in pairs, ovate to broadly elliptical with slightly curved back wavy margins, thick and stiff, 5-12 cm long and 2-5 cm wide on stalks 7-13 mm long, dark green above and covered with rusty hairs below. **Flowers** are white or cream and fused into globular heads with numerous long protruding stamens, 3-4 cm across, arranged in axillary clusters of 4 flowerheads on long stalks. **Fruits** are hard woody brown capsules fused into a globular mass 15-20 mm across. **Flowering** in spring and summer. **Habitat.** Common in taller eucalypt forests and rainforests in various sites from the coastal lowlands to the tablelands in Qld and NSW. **Family.** Myrtaceae.

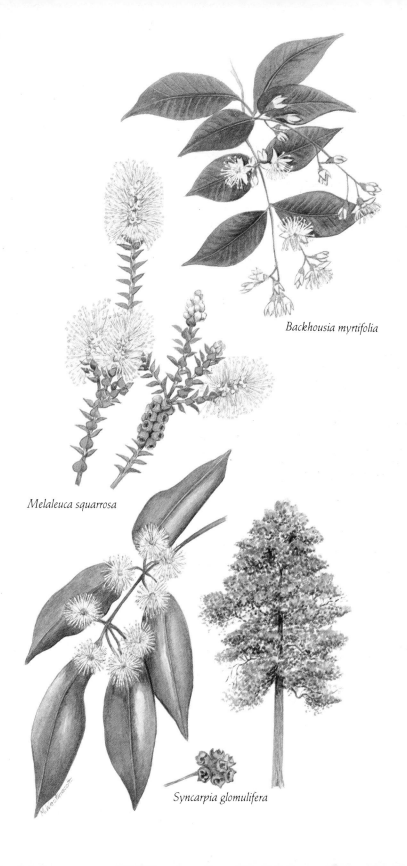

Backhousia myrtifolia

Melaleuca squarrosa

Syncarpia glomulifera

Hymenosporum flavum   NATIVE FRANGIPANI

A small to medium-sized tree 10-25 m high with a cylindrical trunk, slightly flanged in large trees, to 45 cm diameter, with sparse branches radiating in whorls from the main stem. **Bark** is grey and slightly rough with short transverse lines. **Mature leaves** are alternate at the ends of twiggy branches, obovate to oblanceolate with a pointed tip, 7-15 cm long and 3-4 cm wide on stalks 9-18 mm long, shiny green with a sunken midrib above, paler and often hairy below with 8-12 main lateral veins curving towards the tip. **Flowers** are cream turning yellow, fragrant, tubular with a deep pink throat, 3-4 cm long with 5 spreading lobes, silky hairy outside, with 5 protruding stamens. They are arranged in loose terminal panicles 15-20 cm across on hairy stalks 3-5 cm long. **Fruits** are green turning brown, hard pear-shaped capsules 2-4 cm long, splitting into 2 cells packed with numerous flat, winged seeds about 12 mm across, ripe in summer and autumn. **Flowering** in spring. **Habitat.** Open forests along stream banks and in rainforests of the coast and adjacent plateaux in Qld and NSW. **Family.** Pittosporaceae.

Lagunaria patersonia   NORFOLK ISLAND HIBISCUS. PYRAMID TREE

A small to medium-sized tree to 15 m high with a straight cylindrical trunk and a shapely, conical, dense and fairly low-branching crown. **Bark** is dark grey, rough with shallow fissures, the branchlets are grey-green with a scaly surface. **Mature leaves** are alternate, ovate to broad lanceolate, 5-10 cm long and 4-5 cm wide on stalks to 15 mm long, rough, dull dark green above, paler below with a white scurfy surface and prominent midrib. **Flowers** are mauve to rose-pink, tubular, 4-5 cm across with 5 spreading and slightly curved back velvety lobes and a protruding central tree-like column of golden yellow anthers and green stigmas to 3 cm long, solitary in the upper leaf axils. **Fruits** are egg-shaped dark brown to black woody capsules, 3-4 cm long with 5 valves lined with irritating hairs, splitting open to reveal creamy-white to red kidney-shaped seeds. **Flowering** in spring, summer and autumn. **Habitat.** Native to Norfolk Island and coastal Qld, but widely cultivated, particularly along the coast throughout Australia. **Family.** Malvaceae.

Rhodamnia rubescens (syn. R. trinervia)   SCRUB TURPENTINE

A tall shrub to large tree, 3-30 m high with a moderately buttressed and sometimes fluted trunk to 75 cm diameter. **Bark** is reddish-brown, fissured, brittle and scaly with thin reddish bark on the branchlets, downy towards the tips. **Mature leaves** are opposite, ovate to elliptic or broad lanceolate with a pointed tip, 4-12 cm long and 15-45 mm wide on densely hairy stalks 4-9 mm long, green with scattered hairs above, covered with dense greyish-brown downy hairs below with conspicuous oil glands and 3 distinct veins. **Flowers** are white, open, hairy, about 8 mm diameter with 4 rounded lobes and numerous free stamens, arranged in panicles of 1-3 flowers on a short common stalk arising from the leaf axils or the scars of fallen leaves. **Fruits** are green turning red and black glossy globular berries, 4-7 mm diameter, usually with several seeds, ripe in summer. **Flowering** in spring. **Habitat.** Common in rainforests, regrowth areas and eucalypt forests in moist gullies along the coast of Qld and NSW. **Family.** Myrtaceae.

Hymenosporum flavum

Lagunaria patersonia

M. Westmacott.

Rhodamnia rubescens

Eucryphia lucida   LEATHERWOOD

A medium-sized tree, 8-30 m high with a straight trunk to 60 cm diameter and a narrow-domed crown. **Bark** is dark grey to brownish-grey, smooth and often covered with lichens. **Mature leaves** are opposite, ovate to narrow elliptic with a rounded tip, leathery, 25-50 mm long and 1-2 cm wide on stalks 3-4 mm long, dark glossy green above and whitish below with prominent veins; young leaves and buds are covered with a clear orange or brownish resin. **Flowers** are white, rarely pink, fragrant, open, 2-4 cm across with 4 overlapping rounded lobes and numerous free stamens, solitary in the upper leaf axils on stalks about 1 cm long. **Fruits** are leathery ovoid capsules to 3 cm long with 6 vertical segments opening into boat-shaped beaked valves, and persisting after releasing numerous oblong flattened winged seeds, ripe in autumn. **Flowering** in summer. **Habitat.** Common in cool temperate rainforests in central western and southern Tas. and coastal elevated sheltered sites in Vic. **Family.** Eucryphiaceae.

Acacia podalyriifolia   QUEENSLAND SILVER WATTLE

A tall shrub to small tree, 3-5 m high with a slender trunk, low-branched with a spreading crown. **Bark** is grey and smooth, the branchlets are covered with dense rigid hairs. **Mature leaves** (phyllodes) are alternate, ovate to elliptic or oblong, 2-5 cm long and 12-30 mm wide on very short stalks, silver-grey on both surfaces with thickened margins and a prominent midrib. **Flowers** are golden yellow and crowded into fluffy globular heads 6-8 mm across on stalks 4-7 mm long, arranged in axillary or terminal racemes 5-10 cm long. **Fruits** are broad oblong flat silver-grey turning brown pods with raised margins, 3-9 cm long and 10-25 mm wide, ripe in summer. **Flowering** in winter and spring. **Habitat.** Sandy and well-drained clay soils both inland and along the coast of Qld and northeastern NSW. **Family.** Mimosaceae.

Cinnamomum camphora   CAMPHOR LAUREL

A medium-sized tree to 20 m high with a cylindrical trunk and a broad, fairly dense crown with reddish foliage in spring. **Bark** is light to dark grey and hard with deep longitudinal fissures. **Mature leaves** are alternate, ovate to elliptical, tapering to a fine point, 5-8 cm long and 2-4 cm wide on stalks 2-4 cm long, pink when young, turning yellowish green with wavy margins, soft and smelling of camphor when crushed. **Flowers** are greenish-white to cream, open, 4-5 mm across with 6 lobes in 2 whorls and 9 stamens, arranged in axillary panicles among the upper leaves. **Fruits** are green turning purplish-black globular berries 8-10 mm across, seated in a green cup-like structure, ripe in autumn. **Flowering** in spring. **Habitat.** Introduced from China and Japan, planted as a shade tree in streets and gardens and naturalised in wetter areas along the coast of Qld and NSW. **Family.** Lauraceae.

Eucryphia lucida

Acacia podalyriifolia

Cinnamomum camphora

Acmena smithii (syn. Eugenia smithii)   LILLY PILLY

A small to medium-sized tree to 20 m high with a straight and sometimes slightly buttressed trunk in large trees, to 45 cm diameter, and a dense dark green crown. **Bark** is grey-brown, scaly and shedding in irregular pieces. **Mature leaves** are opposite, broad lanceolate to ovate, 2-10 cm long and 1-5 cm wide on stalks 2-6 mm long, glossy dark green above with a sunken midrib, paler below with a raised midrib, lateral veins and oil glands are visible on both surfaces. **Flowers** are creamy-white or greenish, small and broadly conical with 4-5 tiny petals and numerous protruding stamens, arranged in prolific terminal or axillary open panicles. **Fruits** are white, pink or lilac globular berries 8-20 mm across with a circular depression on top, enclosing a single large seed in a succulent slightly acidic edible flesh, ripe in late autumn and winter. **Flowering** in summer. **Habitat.** Common in closed forests, coastal scrubs and rainforests in sheltered sites and along waterways up to 1200 m along the coast and tablelands of Qld, NSW and Vic. **Family.** Myrtaceae.

Syzygium oleosum (syn. Eugenia coolminiana)   BLUE LILLY PILLY

A small tree to 15 m high with a cylindrical and often crooked trunk to 30 cm diameter and a widely spreading crown sometimes to ground level. **Bark** is reddish-brown, scaly, fibrous and shedding in narrow longitudinal pieces. **Mature leaves** are opposite, broad lanceolate to ovate with a long, narrow, pointed tip and numerous oil glands, 3-12 cm long and 1-5 cm wide on stalks 3-8 mm long, glossy dark green above with a sunken midrib and indistinct veins, paler below with a raised midrib and visible veins. **Flowers** are creamy-white, broadly conical, 8-10 mm across with 4 tiny rounded petals, 4 conspicuous reddish sepals and numerous protruding stamens about 9 mm long, arranged in open terminal or axillary panicles. **Fruits** are shiny purplish-red, turning purplish-blue, globular to urn-shaped berries, 13-25 mm across containing a single mauve-pink round seed 6-15 mm across surrounded by succulent pulp, ripe in winter and spring. **Flowering** in spring and summer. **Habitat.** Coastal forests, rainforests, cleared sites and hilly pastures to 900 m in eastern Qld and NSW. **Family.** Myrtaceae.

Cryptocarya laevigata   GLOSSY LAUREL. GREY SASSAFRAS

A large shrub or small tree to 6 m high with a cylindrical trunk and a dense bushy crown of glossy dark green leaves. **Bark** is brownish-black, smooth and finely fissured with raised round blisters. **Mature leaves** are alternate, ovate to elliptical or broad lanceolate, 5-12 cm long and 3-4 cm wide on stalks 2-5 mm long, glossy dark green above with 3 prominent main veins. **Flowers** are cream or greenish, cup-shaped, 2-4 mm across with 6 triangular lobes and 9 short stamens, arranged in short axillary panicles of 3-7 flowers. **Fruits** are red to orange or yellow fleshy globular drupes, 15-20 mm across with a single ribbed egg-shaped seed, ripe in autumn. **Flowering** in spring. **Habitat.** Widespread in or near lowland subtropical rainforests and in scrubs on rich soils along the coast of Qld and northern NSW. **Family.** Lauraceae.

Acmena smithii

Syzygium oleosum

Cryptocarya laevigata

Ficus rubiginosa
RUSTY OR PORT JACKSON FIG

A medium-sized tree to 30 m high with a buttressed trunk to 1.5 m diameter, a widely spreading crown and very low branches. **Bark** is brown to yellow-brown, smooth, but marked with numerous blisters and scattered small scales, exudes a dull white viscous sap when cut. **Mature leaves** are alternate, ovate to elliptic, 6-12 cm long and 3-6 cm wide on downy stalks 1-5 cm long, dark green above and paler below with distinct raised veins and often covered with dense rusty down. Young buds are enclosed in a sheath 25-40 mm long. **Flowers** are enclosed in a hollow fleshy structure that becomes the fruit. **Fruits** are yellow turning red, dotted with warts, globular to ovoid, fleshy, 7-20 mm across, usually in pairs on thick stalks 2-5 mm long, ripe in summer and autumn. **Habitat.** Widespread on dry hills in open forests and dry rainforests in southern Qld and NSW. **Family.** Moraceae.

Gmelina leichhardtii
WHITE BEECH. GREY TEAK

A large, semi-deciduous tree to 40 m high with a cylindrical trunk, usually flanged at the base in older trees and sometimes extending to the lower branches, to 1.5 m diameter, with a widely spreading crown becoming leafless for a short time in late spring. **Bark** is grey, scaly in large trees, wrinkled with powdery blisters in smaller trees. **Mature leaves** are opposite, broad ovate to egg-shaped, sometimes heart-shaped at the base, 7-20 cm long on leaf stalks 15-35 mm long, stiff, dark green above, paler and densely hairy below with conspicuous veins often covered with fawn hairs, young shoots are covered with dense down. **Flowers** are white and purple with yellow markings, tubular with a prominent lip, about 2 cm long with 5 spreading lobes covered with dark hairs outside, and 4 stamens. They are arranged in terminal panicles 10-20 cm long on long stalks. **Fruits** are green turning purplish-blue when ripe, flattened spheres 20-25 mm across with an outer fleshy covering enclosing a single hard stone with 4 cells, each containing an oval seed about 1 cm long, ripe in autumn. **Flowering** in summer. **Habitat.** Coastal scrubs, often on poorer soils, and in rainforests of Qld and NSW. **Family.** Verbenaceae.

Ficus macrophylla
MORETON BAY FIG

A large tree to 50 m high with a flanged and broadly buttressed trunk to 2.5 m or more diameter, widely spreading roots often visible above the ground and a wide, spreading crown. **Bark** is dark greyish-brown, smooth, but marked with numerous blisters, narrow horizontal ridges and scattered small scales, exudes copious milky sap when cut. **Mature leaves** are alternate, ovate to elliptic, 10-25 cm long and 7-15 cm wide on stalks 3-10 cm long, leathery, dark glossy green above and brown below with conspicuous yellow-green veins. Young buds are enclosed in a brown sheath up to 10-17 cm long. **Flowers** are enclosed in a hollow fleshy structure that becomes the fruit. **Fruits** are orange to brown or purple with white spots, globular and fleshy, 18-25 mm across, borne singly on thick axillary stalks 8-25 mm long, edible when fully ripe at any time of the year. **Habitat.** Often begins life growing on the trunk of other species which is eventually enmeshed with aerial roots and killed; widely cultivated but naturally occurring in coastal rainforests in Qld, NSW and Lord Howe Island. **Family.** Moraceae.

Ficus rubiginosa

Gmelina leichhardtii

Ficus macrophylla

Bruguiera gymnorrhiza   RED OR LARGE-FRUITED ORANGE MANGROVE

A small spreading tree to 12 m high with a short, slender trunk, many low branches and numerous stilt-like roots arching from the lower trunk into the surrounding sand or mud and looping out for some distance around the tree. **Bark** is grey and rough. **Mature leaves** are opposite in pairs at the ends of the branches, ovate, 10-20 cm long and 3-7 cm wide with a reddish stalk 2-4 cm long, thick, leathery and glossy green with a prominent raised midrib below. **Flowers** are red and cream, tubular, 2-3 cm long with 12-13 narrow, pointed and fleshy lobes, hairy at the base, solitary on axillary stalks about 2 cm long. **Fruits** are greenish-yellow cigar-shaped drupes about 8 cm long, containing a single seed and usually germinating while still attached to the tree. **Flowering** in winter and spring. **Habitat.** Widespread in saline coastal mudflats and tidal estuaries in NT, Qld and NSW. **Family.** Rhizophoraceae.

Avicennia marina   GREY OR WHITE MANGROVE

Small bushy tree usually to 8 m high, although can grow to 25 m, with a compact, dense, rounded and spreading crown. Numerous peg-like aerial roots up to 20 cm tall protrude through the surrounding mud. **Bark** is light grey, thin, smooth to scaly and fissured in older trees, with white sapwood below. **Mature leaves** are opposite in pairs, broad lanceolate to ovate, 3-8 cm long and 2-5 cm wide with a stalk 8-12 mm long, thick and leathery, bright glossy green above, white or grey and hairy below. **Flowers** are yellow to orange, fragrant, small and tubular, about 8 mm long with 4 spreading lobes and 4 stamens, arranged in dense axillary clusters of 3-5 on short stalks. **Fruits** are yellow, leathery 2-valved ovoid capsules about 5 cm long and 3 cm across, with 1 rough textured seed. They germinate just before falling in spring. **Flowering** in summer and autumn. **Habitat.** Widespread in saline coastal mudflats and tidal estuaries in all states except Tas. **Family.** Avicenniaceae.

Rhizophora stylosa   SMALL-STILTED, SPOTTED OR RED MANGROVE

A small to medium-sized tree to 30 m high with one or a number of slender stems to 60 cm diameter supported by numerous branched stilt roots, with roots looping out from the surrrounding sand or mud for some distance around the tree, and a dark glossy green compact crown. **Bark** is red-brown and smooth on single-stemmed trees, grey and fissured on multi-stemmed trees, sometimes dark grey and deeply fissured. **Mature leaves** are opposite, ovate to obovate, 6-14 cm long and 3-8 cm wide with a stalk 1-4 cm long, thick, leathery and glossy dark green above, paler and red-spotted below with a prominent raised midrib; young shoots are enclosed in a reddish stipule 3-6 cm long. **Flowers** are cream, open, 2-3 cm across with 4 lanceolate lobes with woolly margins, 8 stamens opening in a large valve and inserted in the margins of a central disc, arranged in axillary clusters of 2-16 flowers on a stalk 1-5 cm long. **Fruits** are green-brown ovoid drupes, 2-5 cm long and 2-3 cm across, containing a single seed that germinates while still attached to the tree to form a green cigar-shaped embryo to 60 cm long. **Flowering** most of the year. **Habitat.** Saline coastal mudflats and tidal estuaries in NT, Qld, NSW and north-western WA. **Family.** Rhizophoraceae.

Bruguiera gymnorrhiza

Avicennia marina

Rhizophora stylosa

Leptospermum laevigatum   COAST TEA TREE

A tall shrub or small tree, adopting leaning or crooked growth patterns in harsh
windswept sites, 2-10 m high with a short thick and crooked trunk, erect rigid stems,
a broad dense crown and often slightly drooping foliage. **Bark** is grey or light brown,
fissured and flaking in thin strips from the trunk and branches. **Mature leaves** are
alternate, ovate to obovate or elliptical, 1-3 cm long and 5-12 mm wide, thick, stiff
and dull grey-green. **Flowers** are white, open, 15-22 mm across with 5 separate
spreading lobes around a green central disc surrounded by numerous stamens,
solitary or in small axillary clusters. **Fruits** are flat-topped cup-shaped capsules, 7-
8 mm across with 8-12 valves opening to release very slender seeds. **Flowering** in
spring. **Habitat.** Coastal sand dunes and scrubs, often in harsh windswept sites in
Qld, NSW, Vic., SA and Tas. **Family.** Myrtaceae.

Aegiceras corniculatum   RIVER MANGROVE

A tall bushy shrub or small tree, 3-7 m high, single or multi-stemmed with a large
spreading crown of dark green foliage. **Bark** is reddish brown and smooth, turning
dark grey when old. **Mature leaves** are alternate, spirally arranged around the branchlets, ovate to obovate or elliptic, thick and leathery, 4-7 cm long and 1-3 cm wide
with a thick stalk about 1 cm long, glossy dark green with a prominent midrib
below. **Flowers** are white, fragrant, spirally twisted in bud and opening to tubular
flowers 8-12 mm long and 4-6 mm across with 5 spreading lobes and 4-5 protruding
stamens, arranged in terminal or axillary clusters on stalks 8-12 mm long. **Fruits** are
reddish-green cylindrical, curved and pointed drupes, 3-5 cm long with a single seed
that germinates while still attached to the tree. **Flowering** in autumn and winter.
Habitat. Common along creeks and riverbanks in the upper tidal reaches on mud
flats and poorly drained soils innundated by high tides in NT, Qld, northern and
central NSW and WA. **Family.** Myrsinaceae.

Rapanea howittiana   MUTTONWOOD

A small tree to 23 m high with a crooked, cylindrical trunk to 60 cm diameter. **Bark**
is creamy-grey and smooth with horizontal cracks. **Mature leaves** are alternate,
clustered towards the ends of the branches, broad obovate to elliptic, sometimes
with wavy margins, 4-9 cm long and 20-35 mm wide on stalks 5-15 mm long, shiny
dark green above and paler below, leathery, with a prominent midrib and trans-
parent margin. **Flowers** are yellowish-green, open, 3-5 mm across with 5 lobes and
5 stamens, arranged in clusters of 10-15 flowers along the older leafless branchlets
on stalks 2-4 mm long. **Fruits** are pale green turning violet globular drupes in small
clusters, 5-7 mm diameter on slightly furry stalks 2-4 mm long, containing a single
fawn-coloured globular seed 4-6 mm diameter surrounded by thin flesh, ripe in
summer and autumn. **Flowering** in spring and summer. **Habitat.** Common in wet
sclerophyll forests and rainforests on damp slopes or near streams in eastern Qld,
NSW and Vic. **Family.** Myrsinaceae.

Aegiceras corniculatum

Leptospermum laevigatum

Rapanea howittiana

Lophostemon confertus (syn. Tristania conferta)   BRUSH BOX

A tall tree to 54 m high with a cylindrical trunk to 2 m diameter and a dense rounded crown of tiered clumps of glossy green foliage. **Bark** is light grey to brown, rough and scaly at the base, shedding higher up to reveal pinkish-brown smooth young bark. **Mature leaves** are alternate, crowded at the ends of the branchlets, ovate to elliptical, tapering to a point, 8-15 cm long and 40-45 mm wide on stalks 15-25 mm long, glossy dark green above and paler below with numerous faint oil glands, visible veins and prominent midrib; young shoots are silky hairy and exude a milky sap when cut. **Flowers** are white, shortly tubular, 5-10 mm long and about 25 mm across, with 5 widely spreading lobes and numerous protruding stamens in 5 feathery bundles 15-20 mm long, arranged in axillary clusters of 3-8 flowers. **Fruits** are bell-shaped flat-topped woody capsules, 8-13 mm long with 3 enclosed valves containing narrow wedge-shaped seeds, ripe in winter and spring. **Flowering** in spring and summer. **Habitat.** Widespread on the margins of rainforests and eucalypt forests along the coast and tablelands in Qld and NSW, commonly cultivated as a street tree. **Family.** Myrtaceae.

Endiandra pubens   HAIRY WALNUT RED APPLE

A medium-sized or tall tree, 10-35 m high with a slightly flanged or slightly buttressed trunk to 45 cm diameter and a spreading bushy crown. **Bark** is brown to light grey, smooth or scaly to corky; the branchlets are covered with dense rusty hairs. **Mature leaves** are alternate, ovate to elliptic, stiff, 7-20 cm long and 3-8 cm wide on densely hairy stalks 5-20 mm long, glossy green above and covered with dense rusty hairs below, with distict veins and a prominent rusty hairy midrib. **Flowers** are white, covered in dense rusty hairs, bell-shaped, about 3 mm across, arranged in short axillary panicles 2-5 cm long on hairy stalks. **Fruits** are pale green to deep red globular drupes, 4-8 cm diameter, with a fleshy exterior containing a large globular seed, ripe in spring and summer. **Flowering** in autumn and winter. **Habitat.** Widespread in cool moist valleys close to stream banks in rainforests of coastal Qld and northeastern NSW. **Family.** Lauraceae.

Buckinghamia celsissima   IVORY CURL. SPOTTED SILKY OAK

A small to medium-sized tree, 8-20 m high with a cylindrical trunk and small tufted crown in the forest, but with a spreading rounded bushy crown in the open. **Bark** is brown, rough and scaly; the young shoots are covered with grey hair and new growth is pink to red. **Mature leaves** are alternate, ovate to broad lanceolate, sometimes with 2-5 deep irregular lobes, 7-20 cm long and 3-5 cm wide on stalks to 5 mm long, glossy green above and paler below with fine silvery hairs, conspicuous veins and prominent midrib. **Flowers** are creamy-white, fragrant, small and tubular with 4 curled back lobes and a protruding hooked style, arranged in pairs on stalks 6-7 mm long, forming dense terminal or axillary cylindrical racemes, 10-20 cm long and 4-5 cm across. **Fruits** are dark brown beaked woody ovoid follicles, 15-30 mm long, splitting open to release 1-4 flat winged seeds, ripe in autumn and winter. **Flowering** in summer and autumn. **Habitat.** Rainforests of the northeastern slopes and plains in Qld, but widely cultivated as an ornamental street and park tree in a variety of soils on sheltered sites as far south as Melbourne. **Family.** Proteaceae.

Lophostemon confertus

Endiandra pubens

Buckinghamia celsissima

Clerodendrum tomentosum   HAIRY CLERODENDRUM

A small tree to 15 m high with a cylindrical or slightly flanged trunk to 25 cm diameter and spreading crown, sometimes shrub-like. **Bark** is brown to grey-brown, corky and scaly on old and large trees, with a pale brown underbark; the young shoots are covered with velvety hairs. **Mature leaves** are opposite, ovate to elliptical or broad lanceolate with a pointed tip, 5-13 cm long and 2-5 cm wide on stalks 2-5 cm long, dark green above, paler below and covered with dense, soft hairs below. The veins are raised below with 5-6 main lateral veins. **Flowers** are creamy-white, tubular, 20-25 mm long with 5 spreading to curled back lobes and usually 4 very long protruding stamens, covered with soft down and arranged in loose terminal clusters. **Fruits** are black, shiny, 4-celled oblong drupes, 5-8 mm across, retained in the enlarged 5-lobed red, fleshy calyx which is up to 2 cm across, ripe in summer and autumn. **Flowering** in spring and summer. **Habitat.** Widespread and common in rainforests and coastal wet sclerophyll forests in Qld, NSW and WA. **Family.** Verbenaceae.

Fagraea berteriana   TEN CENT FLOWER

A tall shrub to small tree, 6-12 m high with a single trunk or multi-stemmed, and a bushy spreading crown of dark green foliage. **Bark** is grey. **Mature leaves** are opposite, ovate to broad lanceolate, thick and fleshy, 10-15 cm long and 5-6 cm wide on stalks 2-3 cm long, glossy dark green above and paler below. **Flowers** are pale yellow fading to orange, strongly perfumed, tubular, 7-10 cm long with 5 widely spreading rounded fleshy lobes, arranged in loose terminal clusters. **Fruits** are green turning orange, ovoid, to 6 cm long and 3 cm across with a fleshy outer coat containing numerous seeds. **Flowering** in summer and autumn. **Habitat.** Often begins as an epiphyte in lowland rainforests along stream banks in north-eastern Qld. **Family.** Potaliaceae.

Dillenia alata   RED BEECH

A small to medium-sized tree, 5-20 m high with a cylindrical trunk and a dense bushy crown of large glossy dark green foliage. **Bark** is purplish-red to reddish-brown, loose, papery and flaking; a host for epiphytic orchids. **Mature leaves** are alternate and whorled around the branchlets, ovate to orbicular, thick and slightly rough, 10-25 cm long and 8-12 cm wide on winged stalks, dark glossy green with a prominent midrib and about 18 parallel lateral veins. **Flowers** are bright yellow, open, 6-8 cm across with 5 separate spreading lobes and numerous red stamens, arranged in loose terminal panicles. **Fruits** are bright red capsules opening widely to about 5 cm across, with 5-8 cells containing seeds surrounded by a white waxy covering, ripe in summer and autumn. **Flowering** mainly in spring and summer. **Habitat.** Widespread and common along stream banks and swampy sites in near coastal rainforests and open situations in northeastern Qld and northern NT. **Family.** Dilleniaceae.

Clerodendrum tomentosum

Fagraea berteriana

Dillenia alata

Baloghia lucida   SCRUB BLOODWOOD

A small to medium-sized tree to 24 m high with a cylindrical or slightly fluted trunk to 50 cm diameter and a spreading crown. **Bark** is pale brown and grey, smooth with raised dark brown patches and rusty streaks. **Mature leaves** are opposite, ovate to elliptic or oblong, thick and stiff with 2 small glands at the base of the leaf, 5-15 cm long and 2-8 cm wide on slightly channeled stalks 6-9 mm long, glossy green on both surfaces but paler below with a prominent midrib and veins almost at right angles to the midrib. **Flowers** are white to cream or pale pink, fragrant, cup-shaped, about 2 cm across with 5 elliptical lobes and numerous slender stamens in the male flowers, and a branched style in the females, arranged in loose terminal racemes on stalks 6-13 mm long. **Fruits** are hard brown and globular 3-lobed capsules, 12-20 mm across, splitting at maturity to expose a single oval seed about 8 mm long in each cell, ripe in winter and spring. **Flowering** in winter, spring and summer. **Habitat.** Common in coastal rainforests in Qld and NSW. **Family.** Euphorbiaceae.

Myristica muelleri (syn M. insipida)   NATIVE NUTMEG

A medium-sized to tall tree, 12-30 m high with a straight, sometimes slightly buttressed trunk about 60 cm diameter and a dense bushy crown. **Bark** is brown, scaly or with shallow rounded depressions from fallen scales, exudes a red sap when cut; young shoots and branchlets are covered with rusty hairs. **Mature leaves** are alternate, ovate to elliptical or broad lanceolate, 7-20 cm long and 3-10 cm wide on channeled stalks 10-15 mm long, thin, glossy dark green above and paler below with conspicuous veins. **Flowers** are produced on separate male and female trees, they are cream, covered with rusty hairs, tubular, about 6 mm long on very short stalks, with 3 small lobes and 10-12 stamens, arranged in small axillary clusters. **Fruits** are ovoid, leathery and covered in rusty brown hairs, about 3 cm long, splitting open when ripe to reveal a single ovoid seed with a nutmeg smell when cut, about 2 cm long, partly covered by a red lattice-like fleshy coat. **Flowering** in summer and autumn. **Habitat.** Tropical and subtropical rainforests in Qld, NT and WA. **Family.** Myristicaceae.

Omalanthus populifolius   NATIVE POPLAR. BLEEDING HEART TREE

A tall shrub or small tree, 2-6 m high with a cylindrical trunk about 13 cm diameter and a bushy rounded crown with bright red or crimson old leaves. **Bark** is greyish-brown, smooth and thin sometimes with numerous pimples. **Mature leaves** are alternate, broad ovate or triangular, tapering to a blunt point, thin, 5-15 cm across on stalks 2-12 cm long with 2 circular glands at the base of the leaf, glossy dark green above and paler below with a distinct midrib and lateral veins. **Flowers** are yellow-green to red, very small and arranged in slender terminal racemes 2-10 cm long comprising small clusters of male flowers and a few solitary females at the base of some racemes. **Fruits** are 2-celled glaucous-green slightly flattened ovoid capsules 6-10 mm long, constricted in the middle, with a single ovoid seed in each cell half enclosed in a fleshy coat, ripe in summer. **Flowering** in spring and early summer. **Habitat.** Moist gullies in coastal forests and rainforest margins, sometimes in fairly open country in NT, Qld and NSW. **Family.** Euphorbiaceae.

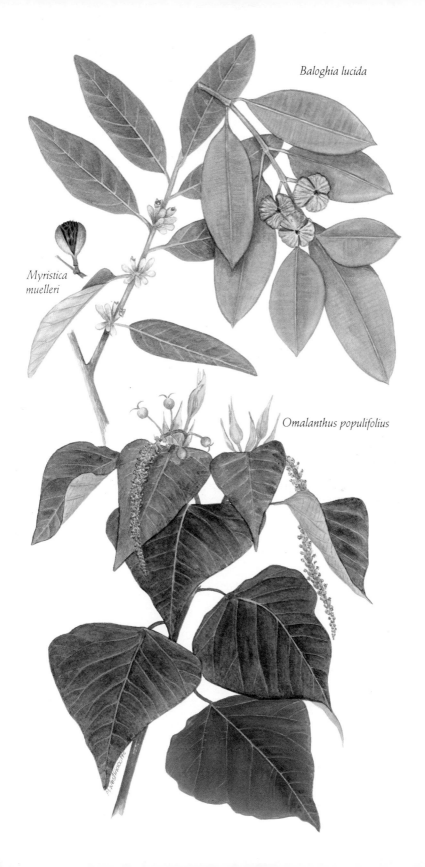

Baloghia lucida

Myristica muelleri

Omalanthus populifolius

Pennantia cunninghamii   BROWN BEECH

A medium-sized to tall tree, 12-30 m high with a crooked and leaning trunk to 90 cm diameter, usually flanged and often with numerous protruberences, and a bushy crown of straggling branches with a climbing habit when young. **Bark** is dark grey or brown and scaly with many corky blisters. **Mature leaves** are alternate, ovate to elliptic usually with a short point, 7-15 cm long and 3-7 cm wide on stalks 8-13 mm long, glossy green above, with many small hollow glands in the forks of the veins below. **Flowers** are sometimes borne on separate male and female trees, they are white, about 3 mm long with 5 round lobes 2-3 mm long and 5 stamens, arranged in short dense terminal or axillary panicles. **Fruits** are shiny black egg-shaped drupes, about 13 mm long, containing a single ovoid seed about 10 mm long, ripe in summer and autumn. **Flowering** in spring and summer. **Habitat.** Widespread in cool moist valleys and along watercourses in rainforests along the coast and tablelands in Qld and NSW. **Family.** Icacinaceae.

Bauhinia variegata   ORCHID TREE. MOUNTAIN EBONY

A small tree to 8 m high with a short cylindrical trunk soon dividing into several large erect branches forming a spreading crown. **Bark** is dark brown with green young branches. **Mature leaves** are alternate, broad ovate to orbicular with a heart-shaped base and a deeply notched tip, 8-13 cm long and 5-13 cm wide, dark green above and paler below with minute hairs, a prominent midrib and yellowish-green veins. **Flowers** are mauve-pink with lighter blotches and stripes, with a slender tube 15-25 mm long, 5 widely spreading delicate lobes to 5 cm long and about 25 mm wide, and 5 long protruding stamens, arranged in compact axillary or terminal racemes of 3-6 flowers. **Fruits** are green turning brown pods, 12-25 cm long and 18-20 mm wide, opening to release up to 15 dark brown disc-shaped seeds to 15 mm across. **Flowering** in spring. **Habitat.** Introduced from India, widely cultivated in temperate to tropical areas and naturalised in Qld. **Family.** Caesalpiniaceae.

Terminalia catappa   TROPICAL ALMOND

A medium-sized tree, 12-25 m high with a short cylindrical trunk and a dense flattened crown with widely spreading whorled branches; the buds and shoots are covered with dense brown hairs. **Mature leaves** are alternate, crowded at the ends of the branchlets, broad obovate, 10-30 cm long and 6-15 cm wide on stalks 8-22 mm long, stiff, glossy dark green turning bright red when old, with 8-12 lateral veins and a prominent midrib, dotted with glands below. **Flowers** are greenish-white, small and cup-shaped with 5 lobes and 10 stamens, arranged in slender axillary spikes 10-25 cm long. **Fruits** are green turning red, flattened ovoid leathery drupes, 2-6 cm long and 2-3 cm wide with a single almond-like edible seed surrounded by a mesh of fibres. **Flowering** in spring and summer. **Habitat.** Along streams in the lowlands and moderate slopes in rainforests and along beaches of tropical Qld and NT. **Family.** Combretaceae.

Pennantia cunninghamii

Bauhinia variegata

Terminalia catappa

M. Westmacott

Eriostemon trachyphyllus   ROCK WAX FLOWER

A medium-sized shrub or small tree, 1-7 m high with a broad spreading shrubby crown and prominent raised glands on the leaves and branches. **Mature leaves** are alternate, spathulate to obovate, often with a tiny point at the tip, 2-5 cm long and 4-9 mm wide, dull dark green above and paler below with a prominent midrib and dotted with raised oil glands. **Flowers** are white, open, 15-20 mm across with 5 separate widely spreading lobes and 10 stiff protruding hairy stamens, solitary or in small axillary clusters on slender reddish stalks about 1 cm long. **Fruits** are small dry capsules splitting at maturity to release small seeds. **Flowering** in spring and early summer. **Habitat.** Locally common in open forests on shallow rocky soils along the coast and adjacent ranges in NSW and Vic. **Family.** Rutaceae.

Bursaria spinosa   SWEET BURSARIA. NATIVE BOX

A tall shrub or small tree, 2-10 m high, usually short-trunked and crooked with a spreading crown of fairly rigid spiny branches. **Bark** is dark grey and rough, with small thorns or spines on the branches. **Mature leaves** are alternate, spathulate to obovate, 1-4 cm long and 3-15 mm wide, glossy green above with a prominent midrib. **Flowers** are cream or white with a sweet scent, open, 6-12 mm across with 5 spreading, rounded lobes and 5 yellow-tipped protruding stamens, arranged in dense terminal pyramidal panicles 10-25 cm long. **Fruits** are dry, flattened, brown, purse-like capsules, 4-10 mm long and 6-8 mm wide with 2-4 seeds. **Flowering** in summer. **Habitat.** Widespread and common in forests, cleared areas, river flats, gullies and some coastal dunes in temperate areas of all states except NT and WA. **Family.** Pittosporaceae.

Banksia marginata   SILVER BANKSIA

A bushy shrub or small tree to 10 m high with many spreading branches. **Bark** is grey and rough; the young shoots are brown and furry. **Mature leaves** are in whorls, becoming alternate when older, spathulate to linear or oblong with a blunt or notched tip and sometimes with serrated margins, 2-10 cm long and 3-10 mm wide, stiff, dark green above with a depressed midrib, whitish below with short brown hairs on the midrib. **Flowers** are yellow, tubular with long, wiry, straight or curved protruding styles when released, arranged in cylindrical upright spikes 4-10 cm long and 4-6 cm diameter. **Fruits** are greyish-brown cylindrical hairy cones, 4-10 cm long and 4-6 cm diameter, with numerous protruding follicles containing 2 flat winged seeds, released on maturity. **Flowering** most of the year. **Habitat.** Widespread and common on a wide variety of sites and soils from the coast to the sub-alps in NSW, Vic., SA and Tas. **Family.** Proteaceae.

Bursaria spinosa

Eriostemon trachyphyllus

Banksia marginata

Macadamia integrifolia   MACADAMIA, QUEENSLAND OR BOPPLE NUT
A medium-sized tree to 20 m high, dense, compact and smaller in cultivation, with a cylindrical trunk to 45 cm diameter and a bushy crown with many branches. **Bark** is brown to greyish-brown, slightly rough with numerous pale corky pores. **Mature leaves** are alternate or in whorls of 2-4, spathulate or oblanceolate, stiff with wavy margins, 7-25 cm long and 3-7 cm wide on stalks 5-15 mm long, glossy dark green with prominent veins; young leaves have serrated margins. **Flowers** are creamy-white, tubular, 6-10 mm long with 4 curled back lobes, whorled around a central stalk to form pendulous racemes 15-25 cm long arising from the lower leaf axils and leaf scars along older branches. **Fruits** are edible globular brown nuts with a smooth hard shell and a soft green covering, to 3 cm across, ripe in late summer. **Flowering** in late winter and spring. **Habitat.** A rainforest tree, although widely cultivated commercially and often seen in cleared areas along the coast on well drained loamy soils of northeastern NSW and southeastern Qld. **Family.** Proteaceae.

Acronychia imperforata   LOGAN APPLE. BEACH ACRONYCHIA
A tall bushy shrub or slender tree to 15 m high with a short cylindrical trunk to about 30 cm diameter and a compact, low-branching crown. **Bark** is brown, thin and smooth with fine cracks; the young shoots are reddish. **Mature leaves** are opposite, sometimes alternate, obovate to broadly elliptical with a rounded or notched tip, leathery, 3-12 cm long and 15-40 mm wide on stalks 5-25 mm long, dark green above and paler below with distinct veins. **Flowers** are cream, about 1 cm across, with 4 narrow lobes 6-9 mm long and 8 stamens, arranged in sparse axillary panicles on a long common stalk. **Fruits** are ovoid fleshy drupes, yellow-orange when ripe in early summer, 1-2 cm long and 6-10 mm across with reddish-black seeds 4-6 mm long. **Flowering** in late summer and autumn. **Habitat.** Coastal rainforests fringing the seashore in Qld and northern NSW. **Family.** Rutaceae.

Flindersia maculosa   LEOPARD WOOD
A small to medium-sized tree to 14 m high with a straight trunk and a spreading crown of graceful, pendulous foliage. **Bark** is grey, scaly and mottled with patches of yellow, brown and orange where the outer bark has fallen off. **Mature leaves** are opposite, narrow obovate to spathulate with slightly curved back margins, occasionally lobed, 1-8 cm long and 5-10 mm wide on a stalk 3-5 mm long, glossy dark green above and paler below, dotted with oil glands. **Flowers** are creamy-white, open, 6-10 mm across with 5 lobes and 5 stamens, arranged in terminal or axillary panicles in showy masses about 75 mm long. **Fruits** are brown, woody, ovoid capsules 25-40 mm long, covered with small sharp projections and consisting of 5 valves opening to release flat winged seeds about 2 cm long, ripe in autumn. **Flowering** in spring and early summer. **Habitat.** Low rainfall areas inland in lightly wooded areas on red soil plains and the western slopes in Qld and northwestern NSW. **Family.** Rutaceae.

Macadamia integrifolia

Acronychia imperforata

Flindersia maculosa

Barringtonia acutangula   FRESHWATER MANGROVE

A deciduous tall shrub to medium-sized tree, 8-25 m high with a single trunk or multi-stemmed, and a dense spreading crown. The bark and stems are used to stupefy fish. **Mature leaves** are alternate, clustered at the ends of the branchlets, ovate to obovate or narrow elliptical with entire or finely serrated wavy margins, 4-16 cm long and 2-6 cm wide on stalks 4-15 mm long, glossy bright green with prominent veins, and shed during the dry season. **Flowers** are bright red, pink or white, about 1 cm across with 4 small lobes and numerous spreading stamens 1-2 cm long, arranged in pendulous terminal racemes of up to 75 flowers to 30 cm long. **Fruits** are ovoid 4-angled capsules, 2-6 cm long containing an ovoid grooved seed 1-4 cm long. **Flowering** throughout the year. **Habitat.** Along river banks, ponds and swampy sites in heavy soils in northern Qld, NT and northern WA. **Family.** Lecythidaceae.

Planchonia careya   COCKY APPLE

A small deciduous tree to 15 m high. **Bark** is fissured and corky. **Mature leaves** are alternate, ovate to obovate or spathulate with slightly wavy margins or with slightly rounded teeth, 3-14 cm long and 2-7 cm wide on winged stalks 5-30 mm long, glossy green above with distinct veins, turning red before falling. **Flowers** are white and pink, 3-8 cm across with 4 spreading lobes and numerous protruding stamens to 45 mm long, arranged in short terminal racemes. **Fruits** are fleshy ovoid edible berries to 9 cm long and 4 cm wide, containing a number of horseshoe-shaped seeds. **Flowering** mainly in spring and summer. **Habitat.** Open eucalypt forests along the coast of northern Australia from Qld to WA. **Family.** Lecythidaceae.

Macaranga tanarius (syn. Ricinus tanarius)   BLUSH MACARANGA

A tall shrub or small tree to 7 m high with a short, often crooked trunk to 30 cm diameter and a bushy rounded and spreading crown. **Bark** is greyish-brown, and roughened with many horizontal lines of pores and pimples in older trees; branchlets are smooth and often blue-grey with conspicuous scars. **Mature leaves** are alternate, broad ovate to orbicular or heart-shaped, 8-23 cm long and 10-20 cm wide on stalks 8-20 cm long attached towards the centre of the leaf, dark glossy green above, scattered with yellow glands, and greyish-white below, often covered with fine hairs, with many prominent veins radiating from the junction of the leaf stalk. **Flowers** are greenish-yellow with male and females on separate trees, both are small and cup-shaped, in clusters enclosed in a broad, fringed, pale green leaf-like bract, 4-6 mm long in males and 8-12 mm long in females, arranged in axillary panicles shorter than the leaves. **Fruits** are greenish-yellow soft globular 3-celled capsules, about 9 mm across, with a number of soft green spikes 3-6 mm long, enclosing a single round shiny black seed in each cell, ripe in summer. **Flowering** in spring and summer. **Habitat.** Cleared areas and disturbed subtropical rainforests on red soils along the coast of NT, Qld and northern NSW. **Family.** Euphorbiaceae.

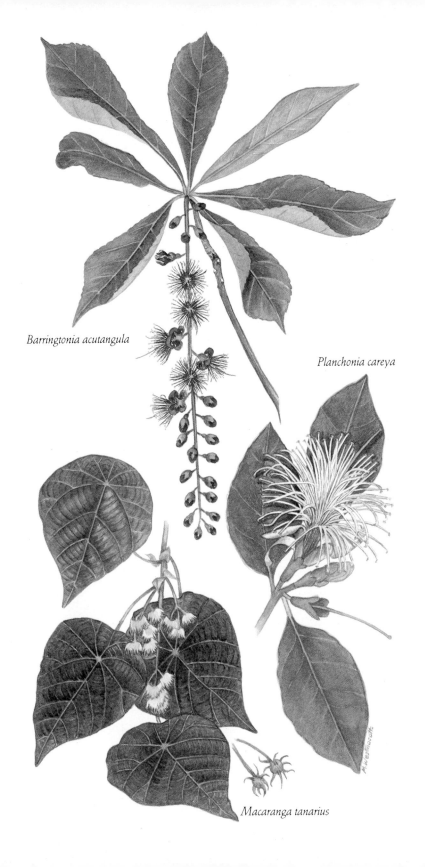

Barringtonia acutangula

Planchonia careya

Macaranga tanarius

Dendrocnide photinophylla   SHINING-LEAVED STINGING TREE

A small to medium-sized tree to 30 m high with a flanged or buttressed trunk to 75 cm diameter, and a spreading crown of large leaves. **Bark** is grey, smooth with small ridges and lumps, often with scattered soft corky scales. **Mature leaves** are alternate, broadly ovate to elliptical with entire or irregularly serrated margins, 5-15 cm long and 2-6 cm wide on stalks 15-55 mm long, dark green and glossy above with scattered stinging hairs on both surfaces. **Flowers** are yellowish-green, very small and clustered in short axillary panicles 4-6 cm long; male and female flowers are often borne on separate trees. **Fruits** are very small flattened nuts, 1-2 mm across, usually enclosed in a fleshy whitish edible mass formed from the clustered swollen flower stalks, ripe in summer. **Flowering** in spring, summer and autumn. **Habitat.** Rainforests of the coast and adjacent plateaux in Qld and NSW. **Family.** Urticaceae.

Dendrocnide moroides   MULBERRY-LEAVED OR GYMPIE STINGER

A shrub or small tree to 5 m high usually with numerous narrow stems and severe stinging hairs on the branchlets and leaves. **Bark** is light grey, smooth with raised pores and paper-thin dead bark. **Mature leaves** are alternate, broadly ovate with regularly saw-toothed margins, 6-30 cm long and 4-20 cm wide on stalks 10-35 cm long often attached to the leaf blade about 1 cm from the edge, dull green and densely covered with stinging hairs. The veins are sunken above and raised below. **Flowers** are yellowish-green, very small and clustered in short axillary panicles; male and female flowers are borne on separate trees. **Fruits** are mulberry-like edible pink to purple fleshy berries with numerous small black nuts, ripe in winter. **Flowering** in summer and autumn. **Habitat.** Widespread in sub-tropical rainforests, particularly in disturbed or cleared areas where it regenerates rapidly, in coastal Qld and northern NSW. **Family.** Urticaceae.

Dendrocnide excelsa   GIANT STINGING TREE

A large tree to 40 m high with a fluted, buttressed trunk to 2 m diameter, with flanges sometimes the whole length of the stem, and a spreading crown of large leaves. **Bark** is creamy grey, smooth on young trees, rough with soft corky markings and scales on large trees. **Mature leaves** are alternate, broadly ovate to heart-shaped with serrated margins, 15-30 cm long and 15-20 cm wide with stalks from 2-15 cm long, pale green and thin, covered with downy hairs below and scattered with rigid stinging hairs on both surfaces and the branchlets. **Flowers** are yellowish-green, very small and clustered in short axillary panicles; male and female flowers are borne on separate trees. **Fruits** are very small black flattened nuts, 1-2 mm across, usually enclosed in a fleshy whitish to dull pink edible mass formed from the clustered swollen flower stalks, ripe in autumn and winter. **Flowering** in autumn and early winter. **Habitat.** Widespread in sub-tropical rainforests, particularly in disturbed or cleared areas where it regenerates rapidly, in coastal Qld and NSW. **Family.** Urticaceae.

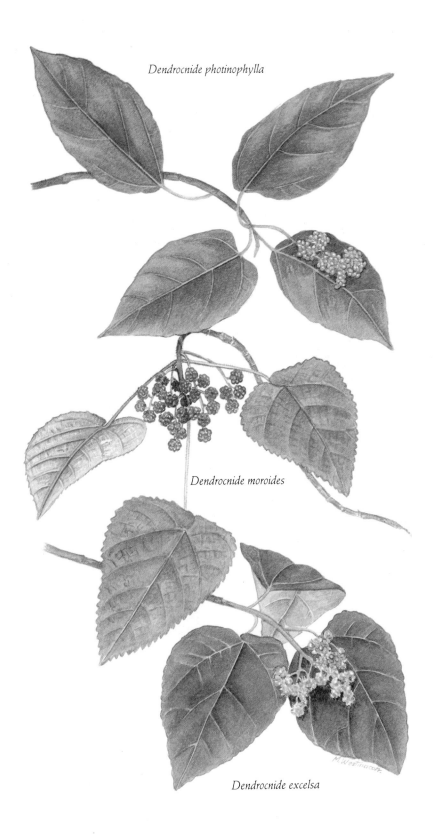

Dendrocnide photinophylla

Dendrocnide moroides

Dendrocnide excelsa

M. Westmacott.

Ficus coronata   SANDPAPER OR CREEK FIG

A small tree to 15 m high with a short crooked trunk to 20 cm diameter, long
sprawling rough and hairy branches and a bushy crown. **Bark** is dark brown,
smooth, but marked with horizontal raised scars, exudes a clear watery sap when
cut; young shoots are covered with stiff hairs. **Mature leaves** are alternate, ovate to
elliptic, sometimes with small teeth on the margins, 5-15 cm long and 25-60 mm
wide on stalks 3-10 cm long, dark green and sandpapery rough above, paler and
smoother below with distinct raised veins. **Flowers** are enclosed in a hollow fleshy
structure that becomes the fruit. **Fruits** are green-yellow turning dark purple, ovoid,
densely hairy, fleshy, 8-20 mm across and borne singly on short stalks arising from
the leaf axils or directly from old branches or the trunk, edible when ripe in summer
and autumn. **Habitat.** Stream banks mainly in closed rainforests, but sometimes in
sheltered sites and open forests along the coast and tablelands in NT, Qld, NSW and
Vic. **Family.** Moraceae.

Hedycarya angustifolia   NATIVE OR AUSTRALIAN MULBERRY

A tall shrub or small tree to 7 m high with a slender, often crooked trunk sometimes
with several stems arising from the base. **Bark** is greyish-fawn and smooth. **Mature
leaves** are alternate, ovate to elliptic or broad lanceolate with irregularly serrated
margins, 5-12 cm long and 2-5 cm wide on stalks 8-20 mm long, thin, glossy dark
green above and paler below with conspicuous veins raised below. **Flowers** are pale
green and inconspicuous, open, about 5 mm across with 6-10 small curled lobes and
numerous stamens, arranged in short axillary racemes on stalks 4-10 mm long.
Fruits are green turning yellow, mulberry-like aggregates of 10-20 succulent drupes
closely packed into globular fruits 6-8 mm across, ripe in summer. **Flowering** in
winter and spring. **Habitat.** Common in moist mountain gullies, sheltered forest
slopes and temperate rainforests of the coast and tablelands of Qld, NSW, Vic. and
Tas. **Family.** Monimiaceae.

Pittosporum rhombifolium   DIAMOND-LEAF PITTOSPORUM

A small to medium-sized tree to 25 m high with a cylindrical trunk to 45 cm
diameter, upward-pointing branches and a compact crown. **Bark** is pale grey and
corky with verticle fissures. **Mature leaves** are alternate but grouped at the ends of
the branches, ovate to diamond-shaped with irregular coarsely toothed margins on
the upper half, 5-11 cm long and 2-5 cm wide on stalks 1-2 cm long, glossy green
with distinct veins on both surfaces. **Flowers** are white, open, about 1 cm across
with 5 spreading lobes, 5 long stamens and a conical stalked ovary, arranged in
dense terminal heads 7-10 cm across. **Fruits** are yellow pear-shaped to globular
capsules 6-9 mm long, borne in terminal clusters, opening to reveal 2-3 black oval
seeds 3-5 mm long, ripe in autumn. **Flowering** in summer. **Habitat.** Common in
rainforests, preferring moist sites along the coast of northern NSW and Qld. **Family.**
Pittosporaceae.

Ficus coronata

Hedycarya angustifolia

Pittosporum rhombifolium

Olearia argophylla   MUSK DAISY BUSH

A tall shrub or small tree, 3-15 m high with a crooked trunk to 1 m diameter, often multi-stemmed, a rounded crown and musky smell. **Bark** is grey-brown, fissured and flaky. **Mature leaves** are alternate, broad lanceolate to ovate usually with irregularly-toothed margins, sometimes just wavy, 6-15 cm long and 2-7 cm wide on stalks 10-15 mm long, glossy dark green above and covered with silvery hairs below with a raised midrib and prominent veins on both surfaces. **Flowerheads** are white, composite, daisy-like, about 1 cm across with 3-5 rays surrounding a central yellow disc of 6-12 tubular florets, arranged in large terminal clusters. **Fruits** are light brown cypsellas, cylindrical with longitudinal ribs, about 1.5 mm long with numerous hairs at the top, about 5mm long, ripe in summer. **Flowering** in spring and summer. **Habitat.** Common on moist sheltered slopes in wet sclerophyll forests and cool temperate rainforests in NSW, Vic. and Tas. **Family.** Compositae.

Schizomeria ovata   CRAB APPLE. WHITE CHERRY

A tall tree to 35 m high with a cylindrical and often buttressed trunk to 2 m diameter and a rounded compact crown of light green foliage. **Bark** is grey, smooth or wrinkled in smaller trees, becoming hard and deeply furrowed in older trees; a thick red gum exudes from cut surfaces. **Mature leaves** are opposite or in whorls of 3, ovate to elliptic with irregularly serrated margins and a long blunt tip, 7-18 cm long and 3-8 cm wide on stalks 9-25 mm long, paler below with distinct cream-coloured veins and a prominent midrib. **Flowers** are small, white and tubular, about 3 mm long with 5 spreading lobes with serrated tips and 8-10 stamens, arranged in axillary panicles 3-7 cm across. **Fruits** are creamy-white or yellow globular to apple-shaped drupes, 1-2 cm across with a fleshy edible exterior enclosing 2 oval creamy-brown seeds 8-10 mm long in individual hard cells, ripe in autumn and winter. **Flowering** in spring. **Habitat.** Scattered in rainforests along the coast of Qld and NSW. **Family.** Cunoniaceae.

Sloanea woollsii   YELLOW CARABEEN

A tall tree to 55 m high with a prominently buttressed trunk to 2.5 m diameter, with the large convex buttresses sometimes extending 5 m up the trunk, and a spreading crown with many erect branches. **Bark** is grey to brownish-grey, wrinkled or grooved with horizontal bands and vertical lines of blisters. **Mature leaves** are alternate, ovate to elliptic with serrated margins and a fine point, 7-15 cm long and 25-30 mm wide on stalks 1-4 cm long, with veins visible on both surfaces, more prominent below. **Flowers** are white, cup-shaped, about 13 mm across on stalks to 35 mm long, with 4-5 egg-shaped furry lobes and 20-24 stamens, arranged in short narrow axillary racemes. **Fruits** are yellow-brown oval prickly capsules, 12-20 mm long, splitting into 2 cells each with generally one shiny black oval seed about 6 mm long, covered with an orange to red-brown coat, ripe in winter. **Flowering** in spring. **Habitat.** Well-drained sites in rainforests, particularly in mountain valleys above 600 m, but also in the lowlands in Qld and northern NSW. **Family.** Elaeocarpaceae.

Olearia argophylla

Schizomeria ovata

Sloanea woollsii

M.Westmacott

Hymenanthera dentata   TREE VIOLET

A tall shrub or small tree, 2-5 m high with many rigid spreading branches, often spiny and with light orange lichen growing on them. **Mature leaves** are alternate, often crowded on short branchlets, narrow lanceolate to narrow elliptic or linear, usually with regularly toothed margins, 1-5 cm long and 2-7 mm wide, stalkless or with very short stalks, dark green above and paler below with prominent veins. **Flowers** are pale yellow, tubular, 3-6 mm long with 5 curled back lobes, solitary or in axillary pairs on slender stalks 2-5 mm long. **Fruits** are pale green turning dark purple globular berries, 4-6 mm diameter, containing 1-2 seeds. **Flowering** in spring. **Habitat.** Widespread from the lowlands to the mountains near riverbanks, in moist gullies and rainforest margins along the coast of NSW, Vic., SA and Tas. **Family.** Violaceae.

Triunia youngiana   NATIVE HONEYSUCKLE. SPICE BUSH

A tall shrub or small tree, 4-8 m high with a single slender crooked trunk or several stems, and a bushy crown. **Bark** is black, smooth to slightly rough with cream horizontal raised pores; young growth is rusty hairy. **Mature leaves** are opposite in pairs or groups of 3-4, lanceolate to elliptical, often with a few small teeth near the tip and a soft sharp point, 5-13 cm long and 2-5 cm wide on rusty or black hairy stalks 3-5 mm long, glossy dark green above and paler below; new leaves are silky silvery pink. **Flowers** are cream to pink with a strong perfume, rusty furry, tubular, 10-15 mm long on stalks to 5 mm long, with 4 narrow curled back lobes and a long protruding style, arranged in dense terminal racemes 5-10 cm long. **Fruits** are bright red to bluish globular drupes with a longitudinal groove on one side, 12-15 mm across with a thin fleshy covering enclosing a round seed, highly poisonous, ripe in late autumn and winter. **Flowering** in spring and summer. **Habitat.** Common in cooler mountain forests, but also found in rainforests of eastern Qld and northeastern NSW. **Family.** Proteaceae.

Pomaderris aspera   HAZEL POMADERRIS

A tall shrub or small tree, 3-8 m high with a straight trunk and an open slender crown. **Bark** is grey and smooth; the branchlets are covered with brown or white hairs. **Mature leaves** are alternate, narrow ovate with irregularly serrated margins, 6-14 cm long and 2-5 cm wide, soft, dark green and deeply wrinkled above, pale green below with raised veins and covered with small hairs. **Flowers** are dull greenish-yellow, tubular, 2-3 mm long with 5 lobes and 5 protruding stamens, covered with short hairs and arranged in long loose terminal panicles. **Fruits** are small brown conical capsules, often hairy, partially enclosed in the dried flower tube, 2-3 mm diameter, with 3 valves opening to release ovoid seeds. **Flowering** in late spring. **Habitat.** Common in forests on moister slopes and near streams in mountain gullies along the eastern ranges in NSW, Vic. and Tas. **Family.** Rhamnaceae.

Hymenanthera dentata

Triunia youngiana

Pomaderris aspera

Orites excelsa   WHITE BEEFWOOD. PRICKLY ASH. MOUNTAIN SILKY OAK

A medium-sized tree to 35 m high with a straight trunk to 75 cm diameter, sometimes slightly buttressed. **Bark** is brown or grey, fairly smooth with horizontal markings and orange-fawn underbark; young shoots are silky-hairy. **Mature leaves** are alternate, lanceolate either entire or with coarsely serrated prickly margins, sometimes deeply lobed, particularly on young growth, and often varying on the same tree, 9-20 cm long on stalks 6-30 mm long, glossy green above, slightly grey below with prominent veins. **Flowers** are white, small and tubular, about 6 mm long, with 4 narrow lobes and 4 stamens, arranged in pairs on slender axillary spikes. **Fruits** are brown boat-shaped woody follicles with a short fine point, 20-25 mm long, opening on one side to reveal 1-2 triangular winged seeds 4-6 mm long with a wing to 12 mm long, ripe in late summer, autumn and winter. **Flowering** in winter and spring. **Habitat.** Common in rainforests above 600 m in Qld and NSW. **Family.** Proteaceae.

Wilkiea macrophylla   LARGE-LEAVED WILKIEA

A tall shrub or small tree to 10 m high with a slender trunk. **Bark** is creamy-grey and smooth with fine scales. **Mature leaves** are opposite, oblong to oblong-lanceolate or elliptical with entire or serrated margins with short sharp teeth, 8-25 cm long and 35-70 mm wide on stalks 3-6 mm long, thick and rigid, glossy green above and paler below with a distinct midrib and lateral veins on both surfaces. **Flowers** are often borne on separate male and female trees, they are yellow-green to orange, cup-shaped to ovoid, about 1 cm long and 4 mm across, with a small terminal opening and fused lobes, the female flowers have thick and fleshy glands inside, the males are more open with 4 stamens. They are arranged in short axillary branched panicles on stalks 4-6 mm long. **Fruits** are black egg-shaped fleshy drupes about 12 mm long, with several single-seeded carpels on a disc, ripe in winter. **Flowering** in winter and spring. **Habitat.** Lowland subtropical rainforests and scrubs in Qld and northern NSW. **Family.** Monimiaceae.

Atherosperma moschatum   SOUTHERN OR BLACK SASSAFRAS

A small to medium-sized tree, 10-30 m high with a straight, often conical trunk, emitting a musky nutmeg-like aroma from the bark and branchlets. **Bark** is grey-green to brown, smooth and often spotted with grey-white lichens, giving a strong odour when cut. **Mature leaves** are opposite, elliptic to narrow-ovate or lanceolate with entire or more usually irregularly serrated margins, 2-10 cm long and 1-4 cm wide on stalks 3-8 mm long, tapering to a short sharp point, glossy green above and covered with dense grey to white wooly hairs below. The midrib is raised on both surfaces and the young shoots are covered with dense woolly hairs. **Flowers** are creamy-white and sometimes pale mauve at the tips, perfumed, open, 13-20 mm across with 8-10 lobes and 8-20 yellow stamens, solitary or in pairs in the leaf axils. **Fruits** comprise numerous carpels covered with long greyish hairs, partially enclosed in a cup-shaped calyx 8-10 mm across, ripe in summer. **Flowering** in winter and spring. **Habitat.** Common in cool temperate rainforests and moist sheltered gullies between 450 and 1300 m in NSW, Vic. and Tas. **Family.** Monimiaceae.

Orites excelsa

Wilkiea macrophylla

Atherosperma moschatum

Salix babylonica WEEPING WILLOW

A medium-sized deciduous tree to 20 m high with a short stout trunk to 60 cm or more diameter and a broad open crown of ascending main branches with long pendulous branchlets and drooping foliage. **Bark** is grey, rough and thick with deep furrows and long branching ridges. **Mature leaves** are alternate, linear to narrow lanceolate with finely serrated margins, 5-15 cm long and 6-30 mm wide on stalks 5-10 mm long, bright glossy green above and whitish or grey below with a prominent yellowish midrib, turning yellow before falling in autumn. **Flowers** are borne on separate male and female trees, they are crowded into yellowish-green pendulous catkins 1-3 cm long arising from the axils of the new leaves. Male trees are unknown in Australia, and the females reproduce from cuttings. **Fruits** are light brown capsules 1-2 mm long containing numerous seeds, ripe in late spring and early summer, but not seen in Australia. **Flowering** in early spring. **Habitat.** Native of China and introduced into Australia where it has become naturalized, preferring damp areas, but also growing in hot dry areas along permanent waterways in NSW, Vic., SA and Tas. **Family.** Salicaceae.

Myoporum insulare BOOBIALLA. NATIVE JUNIPER

A tall shrub to small tree, 2-10 m high with ascending branches and a low densely foliaged rounded crown; the branchlets are either smooth or covered with prominent glands. **Mature leaves** are mostly alternate, lanceolate to obovate or elliptic, usually with serrated margins, 3-10 cm long and 1-3 cm wide on stalks 5-6 mm long, thick and often fleshy, glossy dark green above and paler below. **Flowers** are white with purple spots inside, tubular, 3-7 mm long and 9-12 mm across with 5 rounded spreading lobes, densely hairy inside, and 4 stamens, arranged in axillary clusters of 1-8 flowers. **Fruits** are green turning purple fleshy globular drupes about 8 mm diameter. **Flowering** mainly in spring and summer. **Habitat.** Common on sand dunes and cliffs along the coast of all states except NT. **Family.** Myoporaceae.

Myoporum platycarpum SUGARWOOD. FALSE SANDALWOOD

A small to medium-sized tree, 4-12 m high with a cylindrical trunk and a spreading medium density crown, becoming gnarled and crooked with age. **Bark** is dark brown, rough and fissured, the branches are smooth or rarely with protruding glands. **Mature leaves** are alternate, almost stalkless, narrow lanceolate to linear with irregular small teeth towards the tip, 3-9 cm long and 3-20 mm wide on stalks 3-5 mm long, thick and fleshy, glossy dark green above and paler below with a prominent midrib. **Flowers** are white, often with a yellow throat, tubular, 6-8 mm long and 7-10 mm across with 5 widely spreading rounded lobes, hairy inside, and 4 stamens, arranged in axillary clusters of 4-8 flowers. **Fruits** are green almost dry flattened ovoid drupes, 5-6 mm long containing 2 seeds. **Flowering** in late winter, spring and early summer. **Habitat.** Common on sandy soils in woodlands, mainly in the drier inland temperate areas of Qld, NSW, Vic., SA and WA. **Family.** Myoporaceae.

Salix babylonica

Myoporum insulare

Myoporum platycarpum

Elaeocarpus reticulatus   BLUEBERRY ASH. BLUE OLIVEBERRY

A small to medium-sized tree to 22 m high with a straight, often slightly flanged trunk to 30 cm diameter and a dense crown usually with a few bright red old leaves. **Bark** is brown, smooth or wrinkled with vertical fissures, and marked with numerous irregular blisters. **Mature leaves** are alternate, broad lanceolate to elliptical with finely serrated margins, 5-12 cm long and 2-4 cm wide with leaf stalks 6-18 mm long, glossy bright green above and paler below with conspicuous raised net veins on both surfaces. **Flowers** are white, occasionally pink, fringed and bell-shaped with a licorice scent, 6-9 mm long with 15-20 bristly stamens, arranged in axillary racemes 2-10 cm long. **Fruits** are shiny dark blue globular or ovoid drupes, 8-13 mm diameter, with a thin, fleshy outer covering enclosing a single hard rough seed, ripe all year round but mainly in winter. **Flowering** in early summer. **Habitat.** Widespread and common in rainforest margins, scrubby gullies, sheltered forests and along watercourses in open country on poorer soils of the coast and tablelands in Qld, NSW, Vic. and Tas. **Family.** Elaeocarpaceae.

Elaeocarpus grandis   BLUE FIG. BLUE QUANDONG

A large tree to 35 m high with a tall, strongly buttressed trunk to 2 m diameter and sparse open crown usually with a few bright red old leaves. **Bark** is light grey, slightly wrinkled and finely fissured with longitudinal indentations. **Mature leaves** are alternate, broad lanceolate to elliptical with finely serrated margins, 7-18 cm long and 2-5 cm wide with leaf stalks 12-18 mm long, thin, glossy dark green above and paler below with a prominent midrib and conspicuous lateral veins raised below, and 15-30 hairy tufts in the leaf axils. **Flowers** are greenish white bell-shaped and fringed, 12-15 mm long with many bristle-like stamens, arranged in one-sided axillary racemes 5-15 cm long with flower stalks about 12 mm long. **Fruits** are blue, globular drupes 18-30 mm diameter with a fleshy outer covering enclosing a hard stone with 5 cells, each containing a single narrowly oval seed about 1 cm long, ripe in spring and summer. **Flowering** in winter. **Habitat.** Widespread and locally common on moist flats, gullies and along stream banks in lowland subtropical rain-forests in NT, Qld and northern NSW. **Family.** Elaeocarpaceae.

Callicoma serratifolia   BLACK WATTLE. BUTTERWOOD

A small to medium-sized tree to 18 m high with a cylindrical trunk to 60 cm diameter, a bushy crown and slender willowy branches. **Bark** is dark greyish-brown, smooth in young trees, becoming scaly and shedding in longitudinal patches in older trees, the branchlets are covered in dense rusty hairs. **Mature leaves** are opposite, broad lanceolate to narrow elliptic with coarsely toothed margins, 5-15 cm long and 2-5 cm wide on stalks 4-8 mm long, glossy dark green above, covered with dense pale hairs below with a raised midrib and lateral veins covered with brown hairs. **Flowers** are cream, in dense globular fluffy heads 1-2 cm diameter on hairy axillary stalks 1-3 cm long, solitary or clustered on a common stalk. **Fruits** are small green capsules densely clustered into globular heads 8-10 mm diameter, each containing 1-2 spindle-shaped seeds, ripe in autumn. **Flowering** in spring and early summer. **Habitat.** Widespread in damp sites along creeks, rocky gullies and rainforest margins along the coast and tablelands of NSW and southeastern Qld. **Family.** Cunoniaceae.

Elaeocarpus reticulatus

Elaeocarpus grandis

Callicoma serratifolia

Banksia menziesii   FIREWOOD OR MENZIES' BANKSIA

A tall shrub to medium-sized tree, 5-15 m high with a gnarled and crooked trunk and thick spreading branches at maturity. **Bark** is grey, rough and somewhat crumbly and pebbled; the branchlets are covered with dense thick hair. **Mature leaves** are alternate and whorled around the branches, spathulate to oblong or oblanceolate with regularly serrated wavy margins and sharply pointed small teeth, 15-30 cm long and 25-40 mm wide with a prominent midrib and parallel transverse veins, paler and covered with rusty hairs below. **Flowers** are red and yellow, small and tubular with long wiry straight protruding styles when released from the opened flower, arranged in vertical rows to form dense acorn-shaped terminal upright spikes, 10-15 cm long and 8-12 cm across. **Fruits** are grey-brown tapering cylindrical cones about 14 cm long and 7 cm across, broader at the base with a few scattered protruding furry seed capsules each with 2 valves opening to release 2 flat winged seeds. **Flowering** in autumn and winter. **Habitat.** Sandy coastal plains in the Irwin, Avon and Dale districts of western WA. **Family.** Proteaceae.

Banksia prionotes   ACORN OR ORANGE BANKSIA

A tall shrub or small tree to 12 m high with a short trunk, sometimes gnarled and crooked, and spreading branches giving a fairly open crown. Bark is grey-white, becoming darker and marbled in older trees; the younger branches are covered with dense woolly white or grey hairs. **Mature leaves** are alternate and whorled around the branches, narrow spathulate to oblong with regular, triangular toothed wavy margins and a prominent midrib, 10-35 cm long and 15-25 mm wide, glossy green above, greyish-green below. **Flowers** are orange and woolly grey, small and tubular with long, wiry, straight, protruding styles when released from the opened flower, arranged in dense acorn-shaped terminal upright spikes, 10-15 cm long and about 8 cm across. **Fruits** are grey-brown cylindrical cones 8-12 cm long and 3-5 cm across with a number of small furry deeply-embedded seed capsules each with 2 valves opening to release 2 flat winged seeds. **Flowering** in autumn and winter. **Habitat.** Widespread in sandy soils from the King George Sound area near Albany to the Murchison River area in WA. **Family.** Proteaceae.

Banksia dentata   TROPICAL BANKSIA

A tall shrub or small tree to 8 m high with a short trunk, sparsely branched with a scraggy appearance and spreading branches giving a fairly open crown. Bark is dark grey and rough; the inner bark is blood red. **Mature leaves** are alternate and whorled around the branches, wedge-shaped to obovate with slightly recurved toothed margins and a prominent midrib, 10-25 cm long and 3-8 cm wide, dull green above and covered with fine white hairs below. **Flowers** are yellow, small and tubular with long, wiry, slightly curved, protruding styles when released from the opened flower, arranged in dense terminal cylindrical upright spikes, 6-14 cm long and about 8 cm across. **Fruits** are grey-brown cylindrical cones about 13 cm long and 5 cm across with a number of small furry seed capsules each with 2 valves opening to release 2 flat winged seeds. **Flowering** in autumn and winter. **Habitat.** Near swamps, in heathlands and open sclerophyll forests in the monsoonal areas of northern coastal Australia from WA to NT and Qld. **Family.** Proteaceae.

Banksia menziesii

Banksia prionotes

Banksia dentata

Banksia ilicifolia
HOLLY-LEAVED BANKSIA

A tall shrub to medium-sized tree, 5-15 m high with a short, often crooked trunk, spreading branches and a fairly dense crown becoming more open in older trees. **Bark** is grey, thick, rough and furrowed, the young branches are densely hairy. **Mature leaves** are alternate and encircle the flower spike giving a wreath-like effect, they are broad spathulate to egg-shaped or ovate with irregularly serrated wavy margins with small prickly teeth and a prominent midrib, 6-10 cm long and 3-4 cm wide, glossy dark green. **Flowers** are lemon-yellow or bright red, tubular with long protruding styles, arranged in dense squat globular terminal heads about 5 cm across surrounded by a rosette of leaves at the base. **Fruits** are brownish-grey almond-shaped woody capsules 1-2 cm across, partly embedded in a small woody cone and covered with dense woolly hairs, splitting open to release 2 flat winged seeds. **Flowering** mainly in winter and early spring. **Habitat.** Moist sandy coastal plains in southwestern WA. **Family.** Proteaceae.

Banksia serrata
OLD MAN OR SAW BANKSIA

A tall shrub to medium-sized tree to 15 m high with a thin canopy and sparse foliage, often gnarled and twisted with a stout, knobbly trunk to about 75 cm diameter. **Bark** is spongy, dark grey, with some longitudinal furrows on older trees, often blackened from bush fires, exudes a reddish sap when cut. **Mature leaves** are alternate, oblong elliptical to lanceolate or obovate with regularly serrated margins, often with a flattened tip, 8-20 cm long and 2-4 cm wide, thick and leathery, shiny dark green above, paler below with a prominent midrib and parallel transverse veins. **Flowers** are silver-grey, small and tubular with long wiry straight protruding styles, arranged in cylindrical terminal upright silky spikes, 7-20 cm long and 5-10 cm diameter. **Fruits** are grey cylindrical hairy cones about 13-15 cm long and 8-10 cm diameter with 5-12 protruding follicles containing black winged seeds, released after fire. **Flowering** mainly in summer. **Habitat.** Well-drained sandy soils, often on rocky sites, in open forests of coastal Qld, NSW, Vic. and Tas. **Family.** Proteaceae.

Banksia attenuata
COAST BANKSIA

A tall shrub to medium-sized tree, 4-15 m high with a short, stout trunk, crooked spreading branches and a fairly dense crown becoming more open in older trees. **Bark** is dark grey and rough, and the young branches are covered with soft down. **Mature leaves** are alternate, spathulate to oblong or oblanceolate with regularly serrated margins and a blunt tip, 8-20 cm long and about 1 cm wide, flat and stiff, dark green above, paler and covered with dense white matted hairs below, with a prominent midrib and obliquely parallel transverse veins. **Flowers** are bright yellow, perfumed, small and tubular with long, wiry, straight, protruding styles when released, arranged in slender cylindrical, upright, terminal spikes to 25 cm long. **Fruits** are brownish-grey cylindrical hairy cones tapering at both ends, about 15 cm long and 7 cm diameter with scattered embedded furry follicles each containing 2 flat winged seeds. **Flowering** in spring, summer and autumn. **Habitat.** Common on moist sandy heaths and woodlands in southwestern WA. **Family.** Proteaceae.

Banksia ilicifolia

Banksia serrata

Banksia attenuata

Ceratopetalum apetalum   COACHWOOD. SCENTED SATINWOOD

A medium-sized tree to 25 m high with a straight trunk, sometimes shortly buttressed in older trees, to 90 cm diameter, and a fairly dense small crown. **Bark** is light grey, spotted with darker shades due to lichen growth, smooth with horizontal raised bands circling the trunk. Older trees have dark rough and scaly bark on the buttressed portion of the trunk. Red sap is occasionally emitted from wounds. **Mature leaves** are opposite, broad lanceolate with serrated margins, 3-25 cm long and 1-7 cm wide, shiny dark green above and paler below, on a stalk 1-2 cm long with a raised midrib and conspicuous net veins below. **Flowers** are cream to white turning pink, open, 6-8 mm across, enlarging to about 18 mm across with 5 separated lanceolate lobes and 8-10 short stamens attached to a flat yellow central disc. They are arranged in loose terminal or axillary clusters on hairy stalks 8-10 cm long. **Fruits** are thin woody egg-shaped capsules about 3 mm diameter containing a single seed, and surrounded by the persistent flower lobes, ripe in summer. **Flowering** in spring and early summer. **Habitat.** Warm temperate rainforests on poorer soils in Qld and NSW. **Family.** Cunoniaceae.

Backhousia citriodora   LEMON-SCENTED MYRTLE

A large shrub or medium-sized tree, 3-20 m high with a short trunk and a bushy, low-branching crown with reddish new growth. **Bark** is grey to light brown, rough with small scales, flaking off in irregular patches to reveal smooth light orange to yellow new bark. **Mature leaves** are opposite, broad lanceolate to narrow ovate with irregular shallow teeth on the margins, 5-12 cm long and 15-40 mm wide, shiny green above, paler and hairy below with a prominent midrib, lemon-scented when crushed. **Flowers** are pale green to white, bell-shaped, 5-9 mm across with 4-5 broad spreading separate lobes and numerous long, protruding stamens, arranged in large fluffy axillary clusters near the ends of the branchlets. **Fruits** are small globular 2-celled brown capsules to 2 mm long contained in the persistent lobes of the calyx, ripe in autumn. **Flowering** in summer and autumn. **Habitat.** Coastal forests and rainforests of southeastern Qld and northern NSW. **Family.** Myrtaceae.

Ceratopetalum gummiferum   CHRISTMAS BUSH

A tall shrub or small tree, 4-10 m high with a slender trunk and a fairly dense, low-branching crown. **Bark** is grey and rather rough. **Mature leaves** are opposite, pinnately divided into 3 leaflets radiating from the end of the leaf stalk, they are broad lanceolate to ovate with serrated margins, 3-8 cm long and 6-20 mm wide, shiny dark green above and paler below with a prominent midrib. **Flowers** are white turning red, open, about 6 mm across, enlarging to about 25 mm across after fertilisation, with 5 separated lanceolate lobes and 8-10 short stamens, arranged in loose terminal or axillary clusters. **Fruits** are thin woody egg-shaped capsules about 5 mm diameter containing a single seed, and surrounded by the persistent red flower lobes, ripe in summer. **Flowering** in spring. **Habitat.** Widespread in open forests, rainforest gullies and heaths on sandy soils along the coast of southern Qld and NSW. **Family.** Cunoniaceae.

Ceratopetalum apetalum

Backhousia citriodora

Ceratopetalum gummiferum

Heritiera trifoliolata (syn. Argyrodendron t.)   WHITE BOOYONG

A large tree to 50 m high with a cylindrical, strongly buttressed trunk at the base, to 1 m diameter, and a dense crown with copper-coloured leaves when viewed from below. **Bark** is brown or grey, fissured, sometimes scaly and wrinkled, shedding in irregular flakes and cracking longitudinally. **Mature leaves** are alternate, palmately divided into 3 elliptic to narrow elliptic leaflets with blunt narrow tips, radiating from the end of the leaf stalk, each 7-14 cm long and 3-5 cm wide on stalks 5-6 mm long, dull green above and covered with silver-grey to copper-coloured small scales below, with a raised midrib and 12-15 lateral veins visible on both surfaces. **Flowers** are brown or cream, small and bell-shaped, about 6 mm across with 5 triangular lobes and a fused column of stamens, arranged in much-branched axillary panicles on slender stalks. **Fruits** are dry winged fruits comprising a round seed 8-13 mm diameter attached to a thin flat brown-silver scaly wing about 3 cm long and 15 mm wide, ripe in spring and summer. **Flowering** in winter and spring. **Habitat.** Common and widespread in moist coastal scrubs and subtropical rainforests to 600 m in Qld and NSW. **Family.** Sterculiaceae.

Heritiera actinophylla (syn. Argyrodendron a.)   TULIP OAK. BLACK JACK

A large tree to 50 m high with a straight, tall and prominently buttressed trunk to 1.7 m diameter and a fairly dense low spreading crown. **Bark** is grey to black, rough and scaly, finely fissured in large trees and shed in small flakes. **Mature leaves** are alternate, palmately divided into 3-9 (usually 7) lanceolate to narrow elliptic leaflets radiating from the end of the leaf stalk, each 5-15 cm long and 1-4 cm wide on stalks 5-15 mm long, dark green above with a raised midrib and distinct veins on both surfaces. **Flowers** are white or cream, small, bell-shaped and lemon-scented, 3-7 mm long with 5 triangular lobes scattered with scurfy scales, arranged in loose axillary panicles on short stalks. **Fruits** are globular nuts about 6-8 mm diameter each attached to a flat thin wing 2-6 cm long and 1-5 cm wide, covered with coppery-brown scurfy scales, ripe in late autumn and winter. **Flowering** in autumn. **Habitat.** Common in warm temperate forests and rainforests, often above 600 m in Qld and NSW. **Family.** Sterculiaceae.

Schefflera actinophylla (syn. Brassaia a.)   UMBRELLA TREE

A small to medium-sized tree to 16 m high with a cylindrical trunk to 30 cm diameter often dividing early into 2 or more stems, and a low compact crown of drooping foliage. **Bark** is greyish-brown and smooth with small longitudinal fissures and horizontal scars of fallen leaves. **Mature leaves** are alternate, whorled around the main stems, leathery, shiny dark green above and pale green below with a prominent midrib, palmately divided into 7-16 obovate leaflets, to 30 cm long and 12 cm wide, on long reddish stalks radiating from the end of a thick fleshy main stalk 40-70 cm long. **Flowers** are bright red, cup-shaped, about 4 mm across with 4 rounded lobes that quickly fall leaving a central disc with a whorl of numerous protruding red stamens, arranged in globular clusters about 2 cm across on a stout brown stalk attached to a long thick stem to 1 m long bearing numerous clusters of flowers; these radiate stiffly from the end of each branch like the tentacles of an octopus. **Fruits** are purple to black fleshy and globular, about 5 mm across, containing a single seed. **Flowering** in spring. **Habitat.** Rainforests, sometimes growing on rocks, in Qld, NT and northern NSW, but widely cultivated. **Family.** Araliaceae.

Heritiera trifoliolata

Heritiera actinophylla

Schefflera actinophylla

Cochlospermum gillivraei　　　　　　　　COTTON TREE. KAPOK BUSH

A small deciduous tree to 12 m high with a slender trunk to 40 cm diameter and a small, sparse crown. **Bark** is rather variable, brown to greyish-brown, flaky and fissured with small rectangular scales. **Mature leaves** are alternate, palmately divided into 5-7 narrow lanceolate to narrow ovate leaflets radiating from the end of the leaf stalk, each about 7 cm long and 2 cm wide, dark green and sometimes with slightly toothed margins. **Flowers** are bright yellow with pink spots and stripes, open, 4-6 cm across with 5 notched lobes and numerous stamens, arranged in short panicles borne at the ends of leafless branches. **Fruits** are brown globular or oblong capsules 8-10 cm across with 5 valves opening to reveal numerous small dark seeds embedded in a mass of fine silky, cotton-like hairs, ripe in summer and autumn. **Flowering** in winter and spring when the tree is leafless. **Habitat.** Widespread in rocky areas, monsoon forests and tropical woodlands in coastal and inland areas of northern Qld and NT. **Family.** Cochlospermaceae.

Euodia elleryana　　　　　　　　　　　PINK EUODIA

A medium-sized tree to 25 m high with a cylindrical trunk to 60 cm diameter, sometimes slightly buttressed or flanged in large trees, and a widely spreading dark green crown. **Bark** is light grey to light brown, thick, soft and corky, sometimes with ridges and fissures. **Mature leaves** are opposite, palmately divided into 3 ovate to elliptic leaflets radiating from the end of the leaf stalk, each 6-22 cm long and 3-7 cm wide on stalks 3-10 mm long, tapering to a short point, glossy dark green above and paler below with distinct veins below. **Flowers** are pink to mauve, rarely white, cup-shaped, about 6 mm long with 4 lobes and 4 protruding stamens, arranged in dense axillary clusters on stalks 3-4 cm long. **Fruits** are dry 2-4 lobed grey-brown capsules, 10-13 mm long, splitting down one side to reveal a single flattened globular shiny black seed, 4-5 mm long, in each cell, ripe in spring and summer. **Flowering** in late summer and autumn. **Habitat.** Widespread in riverine rainforests along the coast of northern WA, NT, Qld and northern NSW. **Family.** Rutaceae.

Adansonia gregorii　　BOAB. BOTTLE TREE. DEAD RAT TREE. GADAWON

A small to medium-sized deciduous tree to 15 m high with a bottle-shaped trunk up to 5 m diameter in older trees; young trees have a dense, conical crown, older trees are more sparse and spreading. **Bark** is brown, smooth and slightly shiny, turning dull grey and pock-marked in older trees. **Mature leaves** are alternate, palmately divided into 5-9 broad lanceolate to obovate leaflets radiating from the end of the leaf stalk, each 6-11 cm long and 2-4 cm wide on stalks 1-3 mm long, bright green above, with soft hairs and a raised midrib below. **Flowers** are white, fleshy and fragrant, broadly tubular, about 7 cm across with 5 soft curled back lobes about 5 cm long and numerous white protruding stamens 5-6 cm long; they are solitary and terminal. **Fruits** are dark brown ovoid woody pods with a small point, 15-25 cm long and 10-20 cm across, covered with grey-brown velvety hairs, containing brown to black bean-like edible seeds about 1 cm across enclosed in a light brown powdery mass, ripe in late summer and autumn. **Flowering** most of the year, but mainly in summer when the tree is leafless. **Habitat.** Rocky outcrops on light soils in open woodlands of the plains and tablelands in the tropical Kimberley region of WA and NT. **Family.** Bombacaceae.

114

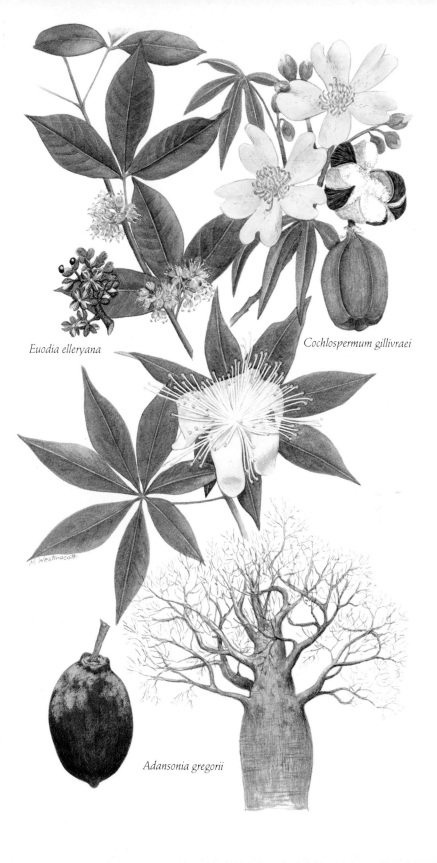

Euodia elleryana

Cochlospermum gillivraei

M. Westmacott

Adansonia gregorii

Aleurites moluccana   CANDLENUT TREE

A medium-sized tree to 20 m high with a short stout trunk and a widely spreading sparse conical or rounded crown. **Bark** is greenish-grey to brownish-grey rather rough with pores and small longitudinal fissures. **Mature leaves** are alternate, often crowded at the ends of the branchlets, heart-shaped to broadly ovate with up to 5 pointed lobes, 10-30 cm long and 8-15 cm wide, pale green and leathery with distinct veins and hairy stalks, aromatic when crushed; new growth is covered with dense rusty hairs. **Flowers** are white, open, about 1 cm across with 5 regular spreading lobes and about 20 stamens, arranged in large terminal clusters 10-18 cm long. **Fruits** are brown globular drupes, 5-8 cm across, with 1-2 rough seeds to 3 cm across, valued for their oil, ripe in autumn. **Flowering** in summer and autumn. **Habitat.** Fertile soils in rainforests and rainforest margins of coastal Qld and northern NSW. **Family.** Euphorbiaceae.

Acer pseudoplatanus   SYCAMORE. GREAT MAPLE

A tall deciduous tree to 30 m high with a straight cylindrical trunk and a broad spreading crown. **Bark** is grey and smooth, scaling in older trees, the branchlets are light brown. **Mature leaves** are opposite, deeply 5-lobed with serrated margins, 7-16 cm across on stalks 4-20 cm long, dark green with 5 prominent veins, turning reddish-brown before falling in autumn. **Flowers** are yellowish-green, about 6 mm diameter with 5 lobes, arranged in narrow terminal pendulous panicles 5-20 cm long comprising 60-100 flowers. **Fruits** are green turning brown dry, single-seeded fruits each with a wing at an acute angle, 3-6 cm long, joined in pairs at the end of stalks 1-2 cm long. **Flowering** in spring. **Habitat.** Introduced from Europe, but naturalised in parts of NSW and SA, preferring deep, moist, well drained rich soils at low altitudes and widely planted as a street tree in cooler temperate climates. **Family.** Aceraceae.

Carica papaya   PAPAYA. PAW PAW

A tall tree-like shrub to 10 m high with a straight, unbranched hollow cylindrical trunk topped with a palm-like crown of large deeply-lobed leaves. **Bark** is grey, turning green at the top of the trunk, ringed with many large leaf scars. **Mature leaves** are whorled around the top of the trunk, palmately divided into 5-7 main lobes which are themselves lobed, 25-75 cm wide on long hollow stalks 25-100 cm long. **Flowers** are creamy-white and borne on separate male and female trees; the males are tubular, 18-25 mm long with 5 thin spreading lobes and yellow stamens, arranged in long axillary racemes; the females are tubular, 30-35 mm long with 5 thick and leathery narrow lobes separated to the base of the tube and curling back at the top, arranged in axillary clusters of 1-3 flowers. **Fruits** are yellow-green turning orange large ovoid berries, to about 30 cm long and 20 cm wide, with a thick succulent outer flesh and numerous black seeds inside the hollow fruit. **Flowering** most of the year. **Habitat.** Originally from South America, but widely cultivated on lowland tropical sites and naturalised in Queensland and NT. **Family.** Caricaceae.

Acer pseudoplatanus

Aleurites moluccana

Carica papaya

Brachychiton discolor (syn. Sterculia d.) LACE BARK TREE

A medium-sized deciduous tree to 30 m high with a straight stout trunk sometimes slightly swollen at the base, to 75 cm diameter, distinctive large pink flowers appear when the tree is leafless in spring. **Bark** is grey to brown, green in the fissures with a brittle brown underbark; the branchlets are hairy. **Mature leaves** are alternate, heart-shaped with 3, 5 or 7 deep lobes, 10-35 cm long and 10-20 cm across, dark green and hairy above, densely downy and often white below with leaf stalks 5-17 cm long. **Flowers** are deep pink to red, bell-shaped with 5 triangular lobes, downy with soft bristles outside and soft hairs inside, 3-6 cm long and 3-5 cm across, almost stalkless in axillary clusters near the ends of the branches. **Fruits** are boat-shaped brown woody follicles 7-12 cm long with a pointed tip, opening along one side to release 10-30 pale oval seeds covered with a fine cottony down, ripe in winter. **Flowering** in spring and summer. **Habitat.** Dry rainforests and coastal scrubs in Qld and NSW. **Family.** Sterculiaceae.

Brachychiton populneus (syn. Sterculia diversifolia) KURRAJONG

A small to medium-sized tree to 20 m high with a straight, stout, tapering trunk to 1 m diameter and a dense spreading crown of light green shiny leaves, sometimes semi-deciduous in early summer. **Bark** is grey-brown, hard and granular with shallow vertical fissures and a mottled orange and chocolate coloured underbark. **Mature leaves** are alternate, variable, egg-shaped with a sharp point, sometimes with 3 or 5 lobes, 5-10 cm long and 2-5 cm across, bright glossy green above, paler below with leaf stalks 1-5 cm long. **Flowers** are cream to greenish with brown or reddish spots inside, bell-shaped, 1-2 cm long and 13-16 mm across with 10-20 stamens forming a central column, arranged in small axillary clusters. **Fruits** are boat-shaped beaked leathery brown follicles 2-10 cm long, opening along one side to release up to 20 egg-shaped yellow seeds held in a prickly outer skin, ripe in winter and spring. **Flowering** in spring and summer. **Habitat.** Widespread on stony slopes in open woodlands and dry rainforests below 1000 m in Qld, NSW and Vic. **Family.** Sterculiaceae.

Brachychiton acerifolius (syn. Sterculia acerifolia) FLAME TREE

A tall deciduous tree to 40 m high with a straight stout trunk to 1 m diameter which emits a hollow sound when tapped, distinctive flame red flowers are massed on the spreading tree when leafless in spring. **Bark** is grey or brown, fissured or wrinkled, with white inner bark covered by net-like fibres. **Mature leaves** are alternate, very variable, 3-lobed and entire leaves may appear on the same tree, they are leathery, ovate to egg-shaped, 8-30 cm long, entire or more often divided into 5-7 lobes, shiny green above, paler below with leaf stalks 7-25 cm long. **Flowers** are red, bell-shaped, waxy, 2-3 cm long and 10-15 mm across; male flowers have 10-15 fused stamens, females frequently occur on the same tree. They are arranged in loose axillary clusters on stalks 7-20 mm long. **Fruits** are boat-shaped leathery dark brown follicles 8-20 cm long with a pointed tip, opening along one side to release numerous bright yellow oval seeds, ripe in winter. **Flowering** in spring and early summer. **Habitat.** Lowland subtropical rainforests and scrubs on moist soils, preferring sheltered sites in valleys along the coast of Qld and NSW. **Family.** Sterculiaceae.

Brachychiton discolor

Brachychiton populneus

Brachychiton acerifolius

Hicksbeachia pinnatifolia   MONKEY NUT. RED BOPPEL NUT

A medium-sized tree to 12 m high, multi-stemmed or with a cylindrical trunk to 35 cm diameter, unbranched for most of its length, with a high slender crown in forest trees, denser in the open. **Bark** is light brown, wrinkled and corky. **Mature leaves** are alternate, stiff, deeply lobed or divided into 16-24 leaflet-like lobes, to 1 m or more long, each lobe being lanceolate with irregularly toothed margins and a sharply pointed tip, 20-25 cm long and about 12 mm wide with distinct veins and a prominently ribbed and winged primary stalk. **Flowers** are fragrant, purplish-brown, slender and tubular, silky outside, about 13 mm long with 4 curled back narrow lobes and a long protruding straight style, arranged in pendulous cylindrical racemes 15-35 cm long on a stout reddish silky stalk arising from leafless stems, the trunk and branches. **Fruits** are red, shiny, oval drupes, 2-5 cm long, with a single edible seed, growing directly from the trunk and branches on long pendulous stems, ripe in spring and summer. **Flowering** in spring. **Habitat.** Subtropical rainforests along the coast of northern NSW and Qld. **Family.** Proteaceae.

Stenocarpus sinuatus   FIRE-WHEEL TREE

A medium-sized to tall tree, 10-45 m high with a cylindrical sometimes flanged trunk to 45 cm diameter and a dense narrow, domed crown, ascending branches and bright red wheel-shaped flowers. **Bark** is grey to brown, wrinkled with short vertical fissures and sometimes corky; young shoots are covered with rusty downy hairs. **Mature leaves** are alternate, variable from lanceolate with wavy margins, 15-30 cm long and 4-5 cm wide, to deeply lobed, glossy dark green above, paler below with stalks 12-25 mm long and raised veins below. **Flowers** are bright red or orange, tubular, about 3 cm long with a globular tip, splitting open to release a long, slender style. They are arranged like the spokes of a wheel 5-10 cm diameter in clusters of 6-20 flowers at the ends of the branches arising from the leaf axils or leaf scars on stalks 4-8 cm long. **Fruits** are grey-brown boat-shaped follicles 5-10 cm long containing numerous flattened triangular overlapping seeds about 12 mm long with a membranous wing, ripe in winter and spring. **Flowering** in late summer, autumn and early winter. **Habitat.** Open forests and rainforests in coastal Qld and northern NSW. **Family.** Proteaceae.

Erythrina vespertilio   BAT'S WING CORAL TREE

A medium-sized deciduous or partly deciduous tree to 30 m high with a trunk to 80 cm diameter, sometimes fluted or flanged, armed with stout conical spikes in young trees, and a spreading sometimes sparse crown. **Bark** is mottled grey-green and yellow turning brown, corky and fissured, the branches are covered with sharp woody prickles. **Mature leaves** are opposite, pinnately divided into 2-3 usually lobed leaflets resembling bats' wings, each 7-12 cm long and 5-12 cm wide on stalks 3-6 mm long with a pointed tip, rounded base, prominent midrib and lateral veins. They are often shed before flowering or during the dry season. **Flowers** are orange to scarlet, pea-shaped, 3-4 cm long with an ovate, grooved standard petal and 10 long protruding stamens, arranged in terminal or axillary racemes to 25 cm long. **Fruits** are brown pods 5-12 cm long and 15-18 mm wide, constricted between the seeds, splitting open to reveal 1-8 red or yellow glossy oval seeds 8-12 mm long, ripe in winter. **Flowering** in spring and early summer. **Habitat.** Widespread in open forests, rainforests and open country in Qld, NT and northern parts of WA, SA and NSW. **Family.** Papilionaceae.

Hicksbeachia pinnatifolia

Stenocarpus sinuatus

Erythrina vespertilio

Geissois benthamiana
RED CARABEEN

A medium-sized tree to 35 m high with a cylindrical trunk to 1.4 m diameter, usually buttressed at the base, and a dense compact crown. **Bark** is grey-brown, smooth and sometimes slightly wrinkled with small blisters, the inner bark is deep red. **Mature leaves** are opposite, pinnately divided into 3 ovate to elliptical leathery leaflets radiating from the end of the leaf stalk, each 5-18 cm long and 2-5 cm wide on stalks 5-15 mm long with coarsely-toothed margins, prominent midrib and distinct lateral veins, dark green above and paler below; young leaves are bright red. **Flowers** are cream to yellow, open, about 5 mm across with 5-6 lobes and 20-30 bristle-like protruding stamens, arranged in dense slender axillary racemes, 8-15 cm long. **Fruits** are light brown cylindrical to elliptical capsules covered with silky hair, 15-20 mm long and 3-5 mm wide, separating into 2 cells each with several flat, winged, overlapping seeds, ripe in autumn and winter. **Flowering** in summer. **Habitat.** Common in rainforests, preferring gullies and stream banks, in Qld and NSW. **Family.** Cunoniaceae.

Sambucus australasica
NATIVE ELDER

A tall shrub or small tree, 5-10 m high with a slender trunk or a number of stems arising from the rootstock. **Mature leaves** are opposite, pinnately divided into 3-5 lanceolate to elliptic leaflets with entire or serrated margins, 3-10 cm long and 4-40 mm wide on stalks 2-12 mm long, soft, light green above and paler below with prominent veins. **Flowers** are creamy-yellow, with a very short tube and 3-5 spreading lobes about 2 mm long, and 4-5 stamens, arranged in large terminal panicles. **Fruits** are yellow globular fleshy drupes, about 5 mm across, containing 3-5 seeds. **Flowering** in spring and summer. **Habitat.** Widespread along the coast and tablelands in moist dense scrub and rainforests in Qld, NSW and Vic. **Family.** Sambucaceae.

Cupaniopsis flagelliformis (syn. C. serrata)
RUSTY TUCKEROO

A small tree to 12 m high with a short trunk, flanged at the base of older trees, to 30 cm diameter. **Bark** is grey-brown, smooth with vertical lines of pale pustules and black underbark; young shoots are bright red with grey woolly hairs. **Mature leaves** are alternate, pinnately divided into 8-14 broad lanceolate to elliptical leaflets, each 8-15 cm long and 2-3 cm wide on stalks 1-6 mm long, with a pointed tip and sharply-toothed margins, shiny green above, paler below with short hairs and prominent veins covered with rusty hairs. **Flowers** are pink to mauve, rusty hairy outside, cup-shaped, 5-15 mm across with 5 small cupped lobes and 8 stamens, arranged in terminal panicles 30-60 cm long. **Fruits** are dark red to yellow-brown 2-3 lobed capsules covered with yellow-brown hairs, 12-27 mm across with 2-3 glossy black or dark brown egg-shaped seeds partially covered by an orange skin, ripe in early summer. **Flowering** in spring and early summer. **Habitat.** Sub-tropical rainforests on volcanic soils in Qld and northern NSW. **Family.** Sapindaceae.

Geissois benthamiana

Sambucus australasica

Cupaniopsis flagelliformis

Cupaniopsis anacardioides (syn. Cupania a.) TUCKEROO

A small tree to 15 m high with a short trunk, flanged in older trees to about 60 cm diameter, low spreading branches and a dense, dark green crown. **Bark** is dark grey-brown, smooth or with raised horizontal stripes. **Mature leaves** are alternate, pinnately divided into 2-12 ovate to elliptic-oblong leathery leaflets, 7-10 cm long and 3-5 cm wide, on stalks 3-9 mm long, with a blunt or notched tip, glossy dark green above, paler below with distinct veins that are raised on the undersurface. **Flowers** are greenish-white, fragrant, cup-shaped, 4-6 mm across with 5 small cupped lobes and 8-10 stamens, arranged in long terminal or axillary branched, pendulous panicles. **Fruits** are bright orange-yellow leathery globular capsules, 12-16 mm across with 3 partially divided lobes, slightly hairy outside, each containing one shiny black seed enclosed in an orange skin, ripe in early summer. **Flowering** in winter. **Habitat.** Coastal sand dunes, scrubs and open dry rainforests near the sea or estuaries in Qld, NSW and NT. **Family.** Sapindaceae.

Davidsonia pruriens DAVIDSON'S PLUM

A small to medium-sized tree to 12 m high with a slender trunk, occasionally with several stems arising from the base, a small crown of large ornamental drooping leaves and flowers and fruits often growing from the trunk. **Bark** is light brown, corky and rather soft and scaly. **Mature leaves** are alternate, 30-80 cm long, pinnately divided into 5-19 opposite, broad lanceolate to ovate leaflets with the midrib and lateral veins raised below, each 7-25 cm long and 3-9 cm wide with irregularly serrated margins and stalkless or with very short stalks. The leaves, branchlets and stalks are covered with dense, irritating hairs, and the main leaf stalks have irregularly toothed wings. **Flowers** are deep pink, cup-shaped, about 6 mm across with 4-5 downy lobes and 8-10 yellow stamens, they are arranged in long, hairy, pendulous panicles arising from the upper leaf axils or the trunk. **Fruits** are purple to black plum-like drupes up to 5 cm across with an acid, crimson, edible flesh surrounding a stone containing two dark red flat seeds about 2 cm long, ripe in autumn and winter. **Flowering** in spring. **Habitat.** Wet and dry rainforests along the coast and rivers in Qld and northern NSW. **Family.** Cunoniaceae.

Grevillea robusta SILKY OAK

A tall tree to 40 m high with a straight cylindrical trunk to 90 cm diameter, sometimes flanged at the base, and a somewhat conical crown of irregularly spaced spreading branches. **Bark** is dark grey, vertically furrowed and ridged with a corky outer layer. **Mature leaves** are alternate, 15-30 cm long, pinnately divided into 11-24 segments, each divided again into narrow pointed lobes 4-8 cm long giving a fern-like appearance, dark green above and covered with silky hairs below with a prominent midrib. Young shoots are densely hairy. **Flowers** are orange-yellow, tubular, 7-10 mm long, splitting on one side into 4 linear lobes with a long looped style, straightening when released to 2 cm long, arranged in clusters of dense one-sided racemes 8-10 cm long of 60-80 flowers on slender stalks about 13 mm long. **Fruits** are dark brown woody boat-shaped follicles to 2 cm long with a long slender beak to 25 mm long, containing a flat ovoid seed about 12 mm long with a thin wing, ripe in summer. **Flowering** in spring. **Habitat.** Gullies, forests and rainforests from the mid north coast of NSW to Maryborough in northeastern Qld. **Family.** Proteaceae.

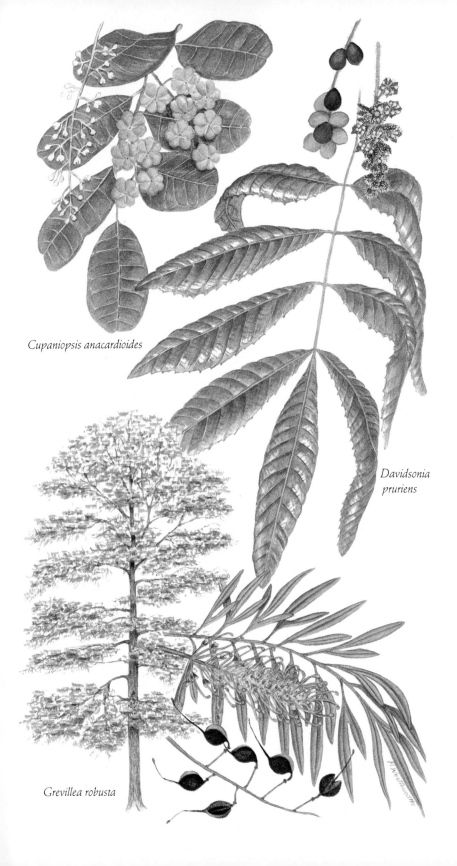

Cupaniopsis anacardioides

Davidsonia pruriens

Grevillea robusta

Toona australis   RED CEDAR

A tall deciduous tree to 55 m high with a cylindrical, sometimes buttressed or flanged trunk to 3 m diameter, and a wide spreading crown. **Bark** is brown or grey, rough, scaly and shedding in oblong or irregular patches leaving slight depressions. **Mature leaves** are alternate, pinnately divided into 5-17 opposite to alternate ovate to lanceolate leaflets, 4-13 cm long and 2-6 cm wide on stalks 3-7 mm long, dark green above and paler below, red when young, with prominent veins below occasionally with tufts of hair on the axils of the veins. **Flowers** are white to pinkish, fragrant, cup-shaped, about 5 mm long with 5 oval lobes and 4-6 stamens, arranged in large terminal pyramidal panicles up to 40 cm long. **Fruits** are dry light brown elliptical capsules, 2-3 cm long and 8-12 mm broad, splitting into 5 valves each containing 4-5 winged seeds 1-2 cm long, ripe in late summer and autumn. **Flowering** in spring. **Habitat.** Scattered in rainforests in moist gullies and along stream banks, preferring rich soils of the coast and tablelands in Qld and NSW. **Family.** Meliaceae.

Dysoxylum fraseranum   ROSEWOOD. ROSE MAHOGANY

A tall tree to 56 m high with a cylindrical trunk to 3.5 m, buttressed or flanged at the base, and a dense rounded crown of dark green foliage. **Bark** is light brown, scaly and shedding in irregular patches, freshly cut bark has a strong rose fragrance. **Mature leaves** are alternate, pinnately divided into 5-12 opposite, oblong-lanceolate to slightly sickle-shaped or elliptic leaflets, 5-15 cm long and 2-7 cm wide on stalks 3-6 mm long, glossy dark green above and paler below with a raised midrib and distinct veins, with numerous oil glands and conspicuous swellings in the axils of the veins. **Flowers** are cream to light mauve, fragrant, 8-10 mm diameter with a cup-shaped calyx and 4-5 lobes about 6 mm long, free for about half their length, arranged in short, loose, axillary panicles. **Fruits** are pink or reddish-brown globular to pear-shaped capsules, 2-4 cm diameter, splitting into 3-4 cells each containing 1-2 ovoid red-coated seeds about 7 mm long, ripe in autumn, winter and spring. **Flowering** in winter. **Habitat.** Common on moderate slopes in rainforests on deep, rich soils along the coast and adjacent ranges, particularly from 300-800 m in southern Qld and NSW. **Family.** Meliaceae.

Flindersia australis   TEAK. CROWS ASH

A tall tree to 40 m high with an irregular flanged trunk to 1.8 m diameter, moderately buttressed in older trees, and a dense elongated or spreading crown. **Bark** is grey-brown, smooth and scaly with short lines of reddish-brown pores, shed in irregular hard flakes to give the trunk a rough, spotted appearance. **Mature leaves** are alternate, sometimes opposite and crowded at the ends of the branchlets, pinnately divided into 3-13 opposite, elliptic to narrow ovate leathery leaflets, 3-13 cm long and 1-4 cm wide on short stalks, glossy green, paler below, with numerous oil glands and conspicuous veins. **Flowers** are white, open, about 12 mm across, with 5 lobes and 5 stamens, arranged in much-branched terminal panicles. **Fruits** are brown ovoid woody capsules 5-10 cm long, covered with short stout blunt spikes, and splitting into usually 5 boat-shaped capsules united at their bases, each containing 2-3 flat winged seeds about 4 cm long, ripe in winter and spring. **Flowering** in spring and summer. **Habitat.** Rainforests along the coast from central eastern Qld to northeastern NSW. **Family.** Rutaceae.

Toona australis

Dysoxylum fraseranum

Flindersia australis

Guioa semiglauca (syn. Arytera s.) GUIOA. WILD QUINCE

A medium-sized tree to 18 m high with a trunk to 30 cm diameter, flanged, fluted or channelled at the base of large trees, and a rounded crown. **Bark** is grey, smooth and spotted. **Mature leaves** are alternate, pinnately divided into 2-6 ovate to oblong-elliptic leaflets, 5-10 cm long and 1-3 cm wide on stalks 1-3 mm long, dark green above, paler below and covered with grey hairs, with distinct and slightly raised veins on both surfaces. **Flowers** are yellowish green, cup-shaped, about 4 mm across, hairy, arranged in terminal or axillary panicles to 15 cm long. **Fruits** are dull green capsules with 2-3 broad slightly flattened wing-like lobes, 6-12 mm wide, each with a thin wall and a glossy brown or black oval seed about 6 mm diameter, ripe in late summer. **Flowering** in spring. **Habitat.** Widespread in rainforests and regrowth areas along the coast and tablelands in Qld and central and northern NSW. **Family.** Sapindaceae.

Rhodosphaera rhodanthema DEEP YELLOW-WOOD. TULIP SATINWOOD

A medium-sized tree to 30 m high with a cylindrical or slightly buttressed trunk to 75 cm diameter and a straggling, bushy crown. **Bark** is grey to brown, very scaly with brownish blisters and shedding in irregular patches, exudes a thick white gum when cut; the branchlets are covered with small raised pores. **Mature leaves** are alternate, pinnately divided into 4-13 mostly opposite lanceolate to elliptic leaflets each 4-7 cm long and 1-3 cm wide on stalks 3-6 mm long, glossy green above and paler below with a distinct midrib and lateral veins, often with tufts of rusty hairs on the axils of the veins. **Flowers** are bright red with male and females often on separate trees, cup-shaped, about 3 mm across with 5 lobes tipped with pink and 8-10 stamens, or a globular ovary with 3 styles in females, arranged in large terminal panicles to 40 cm long. **Fruits** are dry brown shiny globular drupes, about 12 mm diameter, containing a single flattened seed about 9 mm broad, arranged in large clusters, ripe in autumn and winter. **Flowering** in spring. **Habitat.** Subtropical and dry rainforests in southeastern Qld and northeastern NSW. **Family.** Anacardiaceae.

Alectryon subcinereus NATIVE OR WILD QUINCE

A tall shrub to small tree, 5-18 m high with a gnarled and often fluted or flanged trunk and a spreading crown, or a multi-stemmed spreading shrub. **Bark** is dark brown to grey, smooth with numerous corky blisters, becoming wrinkled or slightly scaly in older trees. **Mature leaves** are opposite or alternate, pinnately divided into 4-6 oblong to ovate or lanceolate leaflets, sometimes with toothed margins, 5-15 cm long and 2-6 cm wide on very small stalks, glossy green above and paler below with distinct raised veins on both surfaces. **Flowers** are pink to cream or greenish, cup-shaped, about 4 mm across, with very small broad lobes, arranged in long loose axillary panicles. **Fruits** are green turning grey-brown capsules with 1-3 globular leathery lobes to 1 cm across, each containing a single glossy black or dark brown seed to 6 mm diameter half enclosed in a bright red fleshy covering, ripe in winter and spring. **Flowering** in summer. **Habitat.** Widespread in closed forests in gullies and rainforests along the coast of Qld, NSW and Vic. **Family.** Sapindaceae.

Guioa semiglauca

Rhodosphaera rhodanthema

Alectryon subcinereus

Eucryphia moorei   EASTERN LEATHERWOOD. PINKWOOD

A small to medium-sized tree, 5-30 m high with a crooked, low-branched trunk to 80 cm diameter, sometimes swollen at the base and a spreading crown. **Bark** is grey-brown and smooth with longitudinal fissures. **Mature leaves** are opposite, pinnately divided into 5-13 narrow oblong to ovate leathery stalkless leaflets, 2-6 cm long and 5-10 mm wide on a primary stalk 5-10 mm long, shiny dark green above, greyish-green with white hairs below, young leaves are sticky and emerge from red-brown shiny sticky pointed stipules. **Flowers** are white, fragrant, open, 2-3 cm across with 4 broad papery overlapping lobes and numerous stamens in several rows, solitary or several together in the upper axils on hairy stalks 2-3 cm long. **Fruits** are hard brown oblong to ovoid capsules, 8-16 mm long, densely covered in grey hairs, opening into 6-8 sections to release numerous dark brown flat winged seeds, ripe in winter. **Flowering** in summer and autumn. **Habitat.** Rich moist soils in sheltered gullies of forests and rainforests along the coast of NSW and northeastern Vic. **Family.** Eucryphiaceae.

Boronia muelleri   FOREST BORONIA

A tall shrub or small tree, 2-7 m high with a slender trunk, many arching branches and pale green slender and fragrant foliage. **Mature leaves** are opposite, fern-like, pinnately divided into 7-15 narrow lanceolate to linear pointed leaflets sometimes with very slightly serrated margins, each 10-25 mm long and about 2 mm wide on a flattened, grooved stalk, green to bronze-green above and paler below. **Flowers** are white to pale pink, perfumed, open, about 15 mm across with 4 ovate waxy lobes and 8 stamens, arranged in profuse terminal clusters. **Fruits** are capsules separating into 4 cells containing hard black seeds. **Flowering** in spring. **Habitat.** Forests, heaths and scrubs, preferring sheltered slopes in NSW and Vic. **Family.** Rutaceae.

Synoum glandulosum   SCENTLESS OR BASTARD ROSEWOOD

A large shrub or small tree usually 3-20 m tall, often with slightly buttressed, crooked and hollow trunk in older trees, to 50 cm diameter. **Bark** is dark brown with square scales shedding in irregular patches; young shoots are covered with rusty downy hairs. **Mature leaves** are alternate, pinnately divided into 5-11 oblanceolate to elliptic leaflets each 5-8 cm long and 15-30 mm wide on stalks to 6 mm long, glossy dark green above and paler below with tufts of hair on the midrib where it joins the lateral veins below. **Flowers** are white to pale pink, sweetly perfumed, about 6 mm across with 4-5 oval lobes and a cylindrical tube of fused stamens, arranged in short axillary panicles about 2 cm long. **Fruits** are red and green, leathery, usually 3-celled capsules about 2 cm across with 2 flattened seeds in each cell, about 6 mm across and covered by fleshy red skin, ripe mainly in spring. **Flowering** most of the year. **Habitat.** Common and widespread in forests and rainforests in wet sites and on poorer sandy soils near the sea in Qld and NSW. **Family.** Meliaceae.

Eucryphia moorei

Boronia muelleri

Synoum glandulosum

Castanospermum australe   BLACK BEAN. MORETON BAY CHESTNUT

A large tree to 40 m high with a straight trunk to 1.2 m diameter and a dense crown of glossy dark green foliage. **Bark** is dark brown to grey with longitudinal lines of grey blotches, smooth to slightly rough and wrinkled with shiny dark brown under-bark. **Mature leaves** are alternate, 20-45 cm long, pinnately divided into 8-17 mostly alternate narrowly elliptical leaflets each 7-12 cm long and 2-6 cm wide with a blunt tip, distinct veins raised on the undersurface and stalks about 6 mm long. They are smooth shiny green on both surfaces but paler below. **Flowers** are greenish-yellow changing to orange-red, pea-like with a broad, curved back and notched standard petal, 3-5 cm long with 8-10 protruding yellow stamens. They are arranged in racemes 5-15 cm long, arising from the leaf axils or the scars of fallen leaves. **Fruits** are shiny brown hard cylindrical pods, 10-25 cm long and about 5 cm wide, splitting open to release 3-5 spherical brown seeds each 3-5 cm across separated by spongy partitions, ripe in summer and autumn. **Flowering** in spring. **Habitat.** Stream banks in sheltered positions in riverine rainforests and level sites on mountain sides in Qld and northern NSW. **Family.** Papilionaceae.

Lepiderema pulchella (syn. L. punctulata)   FINE-LEAVED TUCKEROO

A tall shrub or small tree to 15 m high with a short trunk to 40 cm diameter, slightly flanged in older trees, and a low rounded bushy crown of light green foliage. **Bark** is grey and smooth, sometimes with fine horizontal raised rings. **Mature leaves** are alternate, pinnately divided into 4-8 lanceolate to ovate leaflets, 5-10 cm long and 2-5 cm wide on stalks 6-12 mm long, thin and leathery, glossy light green and dotted with minute oil glands. **Flowers** are yellow-orange, open, about 6 mm across with 5 rounded lobes and 8 yellow-tipped stamens, arranged in slender axillary racemes 5-10 cm long. **Fruits** are smooth orange pear-shaped capsules, about 1 cm across, with 3 lobes each containing a single dark brown flattened elliptical grooved seed 6-9 mm long, partly covered by a yellow coat, ripe in summer. **Flowering** in spring. **Habitat.** Rainforests of the coast and adjacent ranges in Qld and northern NSW. **Family.** Sapindaceae.

Harpullia pendula   TULIPWOOD

A small to medium-sized tree to 28 m high with an irregular sometimes fluted and buttressed trunk to 60 cm diameter and a dense, spreading crown. **Bark** is grey, smooth but with scales shedding in long flakes revealing corky blisters. **Mature leaves** are alternate, pinnately divided into 3-8 narrowly elliptic leaflets each 5-12 cm long on stalks 3-5 mm long, glossy green above and paler below with distinct veins and a raised midrib on both surfaces. Young shoots are reddish brown and downy. **Flowers** are white to greenish-yellow, open, finely-hairy, about 15 mm across on stalks about 6 mm long, with 5 oval lobes and 5-8 stamens and a spirally-twisted style, arranged in narrow axillary panicles. **Fruits** are bright yellow or orange 2-lobed capsules, each lobe is 13-18 mm diameter and splits open to reveal 1-2 shiny dark brown or black oval seeds about 13 mm long, ripe in spring. **Flowering** in summer. **Habitat.** Coastal scrubs and rainforests in Qld and northern NSW. **Family.** Sapindaceae.

Castanospermum australe

Lepiderema pulchella

Harpullia pendula

Melia azedarach   WHITE CEDAR. PERSIAN LILAC

A tall deciduous tree to 50 m high, shorter and more spreading in cultivation, with a cylindrical trunk to 160 cm diameter and a dense bushy crown. **Bark** is dark brown with greyish ridges giving a striped effect, prominently fissured or slightly furrowed and layered; branchlets are thick, brown and often wrinkled with scattered raised pores. **Mature leaves** are alternate, bipinnately divided into numerous opposite narrow ovate to lanceolate prominently toothed, lobed or entire leaflets, each 2-7 cm long and 1-3 cm wide on stalks 2-6 mm long, glossy green above and paler below with distinct veins and raised midrib. **Flowers** are lilac, fragrant, about 18 mm wide with 5-6 spreading spathulate lobes 8-15 mm long and a purple tube of joined stamens about 8 mm long, fringed at the tip, arranged in large loose axillary panicles 10-15 cm long. **Fruits** are pale green turning yellowish-brown ovoid drupes, 12-20 mm long, with a succulent covering enclosing a hard oval ribbed stone with 5 cells each with a single seed, ripe in autumn and winter when the trees are leafless. **Flowering** in spring. **Habitat.** Forests, rainforests and rainforest margins on good soils along the coast of WA, Qld and NSW. **Family.** Meliaceae.

Pararchidendron pruinosum (syn. Abarema sapindoides)   SNOW-WOOD

A small tree to 15 m high with a cylindrical trunk to 35 cm diameter and a bushy crown of lacy leaves. **Bark** is dark reddish-brown with numerous corky blisters; branchlets are grey and slightly downy with reddish young foliage. **Mature leaves** are alternate, bipinnately divided with 1-3 pairs of opposite secondary leaf stalks each with 5-11 alternate, lanceolate leaflets with a fine point, each 2-6 cm long and 13-20 mm wide on stalks to 2 mm long, with a small gland 10-25 mm below the first pair of secondary leaf stalks. **Flowers** are greenish-white to yellow-brown, tubular, 10-13 mm long on stalks about 3 mm long, with 4-5 slightly curled back lobes and numerous long protruding stamens, arranged in globular axillary heads 2-4 cm across. **Fruits** are twisted, flattened, smooth green turning yellow-brown pods, 7-10 cm long and 10-26 mm wide, red inside with several glossy black seeds about 8 mm long, ripe in autumn and winter. **Flowering** in spring and summer. **Habitat.** Rainforests along the coast of Qld and central and northern NSW. **Family.** Mimosaceae.

Acacia mearnsii   LATE BLACK WATTLE

A large shrub or small tree, 5-25 m high with a cylindrical trunk and a spreading crown of dark green foliage. **Bark** is brownish-black, hard and fissured, smoother on the younger branches. **Mature leaves** (phyllodes) are 8-12 cm long, bipinnately divided into 8-25 pairs of secondary leaf stalks each with 15-70 pairs of oblong leaflets 1-3 mm long, glossy dark green above and paler below with downy hairs; small hairy glands are irregularly spaced along the main leaf stalk, the leaf stalks are hairy and slightly ribbed. **Flowers** are pale yellow strongly perfumed and densely clustered into globular fluffy heads about 5 mm across on hairy stalks, arranged in irregular dense terminal or axillary racemes 8-12 cm long. **Fruits** are green turning yellow-brown to black straight hairy pods, 5-15 cm long and 4-10 mm wide, constricted between the seeds. **Flowering** in late spring and early summer. **Habitat.** Common on hilly sites in forests and woodlands especially on drier shallower soils, along the coast of Qld, central and southern NSW, Vic., SA and Tas. **Family.** Mimosaceae.

Melia azedarach

Pararchidendron pruinosum

Acacia mearnsii

Acacia dealbata   SILVER WATTLE

A large shrub to medium-sized tree, 2-30 m high, with a slender trunk and a well-developed conical rounded crown on good sites. **Bark** is grey-green turning dark brown, often with silvery mottled patches, hard and moderately fissured at the base in old trees, thinner and smoother on young stems. **Mature leaves** (phyllodes) are bipinnately divided into 8-25 pairs of secondary leaf stalks about 3 cm long with a gland at the base, each with 17-50 pairs of narrow linear leaflets 2-5 mm long and 0.5-1.5 mm wide, dusty green or silvery grey on both surfaces. **Flowers** are yellow and crowded into fluffy globular heads about 1 cm across on stalks about 1 cm long, arranged in dense racemes forming a terminal panicle 6-10 cm long. **Fruits** are straight or slightly curved flat purplish-brown pods with a bluish bloom becoming ashy grey, 3-10 cm long and 7-13 mm wide. **Flowering** in late winter and spring. **Habitat.** Widespread in open forests on the tablelands and foothills along stream banks in NSW, Vic., SA and Tas. **Family.** Mimosaceae.

Acacia baileyana   COOTAMUNDRA WATTLE

A large shrub to small tree, 5-10 m high, with a short slender trunk and a pyramidal crown with branches at ground level in young trees, becoming dense and rounded in older trees. **Bark** is mealy-blue turning grey. **Mature leaves** (phyllodes) are bipinnately divided into 3-4 pairs of secondary leaf stalks each with 10-25 pairs of narrow linear leaflets 4-8 mm long and about 2 mm wide, grey-green to silvery-blue on both surfaces. **Flowers** are yellow and crowded into fluffy globular heads about 7 mm across on stalks about 1 cm long, arranged in long, slender axillary or terminal racemes. **Fruits** are straight or slightly curved flat purplish-brown pods with a bluish bloom, 3-9 cm long and 5-14 mm wide. **Flowering** in late winter and spring. **Habitat.** Moist sites in cool, hilly locations; a native of the Cootamundra and Wagga-Wagga area of NSW, but commonly cultivated and naturalised in Vic. and SA. **Family.** Mimosaceae.

Acacia decurrens   EARLY BLACK OR GREEN WATTLE

A large shrub to small tree, 4-15 m high, with a slender trunk and a spreading, pyramidal or rounded crown. **Bark** is dark grey, almost black. **Mature leaves** (phyllodes) are bipinnately divided into 4-12 pairs of secondary leaf stalks with a gland below each pair, each with 15-35 pairs of narrow linear leaflets 5-14 mm long and 1 mm wide, dark green on both surfaces; young stems have longitudinal wing-like ridges. **Flowers** are yellow and crowded into fluffy globular heads about 5 mm across on stalks about 1 cm long, arranged in dense racemes forming a terminal panicle. **Fruits** are slightly curved brown pods slightly constricted between the seeds, 5-10 cm long and 4-8 mm wide. **Flowering** in late winter and spring. **Habitat.** Widespread in drier open forests and open country in cool moist sites of the coast and tablelands in southern Qld, NSW, Vic., SA, WA and Tas. **Family.** Mimosaceae.

Acacia baileyana

Acacia dealbata

Acacia decurrens

M.Westington.

Archidendron muellerianum (syn. Abarema m.)   SMALL LACE FLOWER

A small tree to 20 m high with a cylindrical trunk to 60 cm diameter, slightly buttressed in older trees, and a bushy crown. **Bark** is grey to light grey, rough and scaly on large trees, with vertical cracks; the branchlets are grey to reddish-brown and hairy towards the tips. **Mature leaves** are alternate, bipinnately divided with 2-4 broad lanceolate to ovate leaflets on each secondary leaf stalk, each leaflet being 3-13 cm long and 1-3 cm wide on hairy stalks 1-3 mm long, paler with raised veins and often with a hairy midrib below. **Flowers** are white to greenish, tubular, stalkless, about 6 mm long with numerous long protruding stamens, arranged in loose, globular, axillary heads 25-35 mm across. **Fruits** are red, wrinkled and twisted hard and leathery pods, 8-13 cm long and 10-15 mm wide, opening to reveal black glossy oval seeds about 1 cm long embedded in orange pith, ripe in autumn and winter. **Flowering** in summer. **Habitat.** Scattered in rainforests of southern Qld and northern NSW. **Family.** Mimosaceae.

Archidendron grandiflorum (syn. Abarema g.)   PINK LACE FLOWER

A small tree to 16 m high with an irregular, slightly fluted trunk to 50 cm diameter and a spreading, bushy crown. **Bark** is dark brown, smooth and shedding in square plates exposing a whitish surface with dark brown patches, often covered in lichen; branchlets are purple-green turning fawn. **Mature leaves** are alternate, bipinnately divided into 2-4 pairs of secondary leaf stalks each with 2-6 pairs of broad lanceolate to ovate pointed leaflets, each leaflet being 3-10 cm long and 1-4 cm wide, on purple-black stalks 3-5 mm long with a peg-like gland between the stalks, paler with prominent veins below and a raised midrib on both surfaces. **Flowers** are rich crimson with a white base and strongly perfumed at night, tubular and stalkless, 18-26 mm long with 4-5 lobes and numerous long protruding stamens, arranged in globular axillary heads 6-8 cm across. **Fruits** are thick, woody, spirally twisted pods, 10-15 cm long and 2-3 cm wide, opening to reveal black glossy oval seeds about 1 cm long embedded in red to orange pith, ripe in autumn. **Flowering** in summer. **Habitat.** Widespread and scattered in rainforests of Qld and northern NSW. **Family.** Mimosaceae.

Archidendron hendersonii (syn. Abarema h.)   WHITE LACE FLOWER

A small tree to 18 m high with a cylindrical, slightly buttressed trunk to 60 cm diameter and a rounded, bushy crown. **Bark** is light brown, corky, either scaly or smooth with numerous vertical rows of pores; branchlets are thick, brown and often wrinkled. **Mature leaves** are alternate, bipinnately divided into 1-2 pairs of secondary leaf stalks each usually with 6 broad lanceolate to ovate leaflets, 5-10 cm long and 20-35 mm wide, on brown wrinkled stalks 2 mm long, dark green with distinct veins on both surfaces. **Flowers** are creamy-white, tubular with short stalks, about 15 mm long with numerous long protruding stamens, arranged in axillary pairs or globular terminal panicles 5-6 cm across. **Fruits** are thick, woody, curved orange pods, 7-10 cm long and about 12 mm wide, opening to reveal black glossy oval seeds about 8 mm long embedded in red pith, ripe in winter and spring. **Flowering** in summer. **Habitat.** Widespread in rainforests of Qld and northern NSW. **Family.** Mimosaceae.

Archidendron muellerianum

Archidendron grandiflorum

Archidendron hendersonii

Eucalyptus citriodora   LEMON-SCENTED GUM

A tall tree to 50 m high with a shaft-like trunk about 1.2 m diameter and a fairly symmetrical spreading, sparsely foliaged crown. **Bark** is pale powdery-grey to pinkish, smooth and dimpled, peeling annually in flakes to expose a creamy-white surface. **Mature leaves** are alternate, narrow lanceolate with a short stalk and prominent midrib, 8-18 cm long and 5-25 mm wide, with a strong lemon smell when crushed. **Flowers** are creamy-white, about 2 cm across, comprising many stamens spreading from a central disc, and covered by a hemispherical cap in bud, grouped in 3-5 flowers, but arranged in large terminal clusters on stalks 2-3 cm long. **Buds** are club-shaped, 7-12 mm long and 4-8 mm across. **Fruits** are urn-shaped woody capsules, often warty, 7-15 mm long and 7-11 mm across with 3 or 4 deeply enclosed valves. **Flowering** in winter and spring. **Habitat.** Naturally occurring in open forests, dry ridges and plateaux of coastal sub-tropical Qld from Maryborough to Mackay and up to 400 km inland; widely cultivated throughout Australia in a variety of soils and conditions. **Family.** Myrtaceae.

Eucalyptus ficifolia   RED-FLOWERING GUM

A small tree to 15 m high with a short thick trunk and a heavily branched broad leafy crown with spectacular red flowers in summer. **Bark** is light grey to dark brown, rough, scaly, short-fibred and persistent. **Mature leaves** are alternate, ovate to broad lanceolate, 8-15 cm long and 3-5 cm wide on a stout stalk to 15 mm long, glossy dark green and paler below, leathery with a prominent midrib and widely-spreading veins. **Flowers** are crimson to scarlet, pink or white, to 4 cm across, comprising many stamens spreading from a central disc, and covered by a hemispherical to conical cap in bud, arranged in large terminal panicles often 25-35 cm across, of 3-7 flowered clusters on angular stalks. **Buds** are cylindrical to conical, 20-25 mm long and about 13 mm across. **Fruits** are urn-shaped woody capsules to 35 mm long and 3 cm across with deeply enclosed valves. **Flowering** mainly in summer. **Habitat.** Naturally occurring on sandy soils near the southern coast in the Albany district of WA, but widely planted in temperate Australia. **Family.** Myrtaceae.

Eucalyptus cladocalyx   SUGAR GUM

A medium-size to tall tree, 15-35 m high with a straight trunk to 1.5 m diameter and a fairly open crown with the foliage usually clustered at the ends of long, erect branches. **Bark** is grey, smooth and shed in irregular patches producing a mottled effect of grey, brown, yellow and orange patches. **Mature leaves** are alternate, narrow to broad lanceolate with a short stalk and prominent midrib, 9-15 cm long and 20-25 mm wide, glossy dark green, but slightly paler below with new growth sometimes reddish. **Flowers** are white to creamy-yellow, about 15 mm across, comprising many stamens spreading from a central disc, and covered by a hemispherical cap with a small pointed tip in bud, arranged in axillary clusters of 5-16 flowers on stalks to 13 mm long. **Buds** are elongated, becoming ribbed when dry, 8-10 mm long and 3-5 mm across. **Fruits** are barrel to urn-shaped woody capsules, ribbed when dry, 9-16 mm long and 6-10 mm across with 3 or 4 deeply enclosed valves. **Flowering** in summer and autumn. **Habitat.** Naturally occurring in open forests and woodlands in the Flinders Ranges, Kangaroo Island and Eyre Peninsula in SA; widely planted in temperate Australia along roadsides and as windbreaks on farms. **Family.** Myrtaceae.

Eucalyptus citriodora

Eucalyptus ficifolia

Eucalyptus cladocalyx

Eucalyptus flocktoniae — MERRIT

A mallee or small tree to 15 m high with a single trunk or a number of slender stems arising from an underground woody rootstock, and a dense pyramidal or flat-topped crown. **Bark** is cream to light grey and smooth, peeling in late summer to reveal light brown fresh bark and leaving some persistent rough bark at the base of the trunk. **Mature leaves** are alternate, lanceolate to sickle-shaped, 8-15 cm long and 1-3 cm wide on stalks 10-25 mm long, glossy dark green with a prominent midrib and oil glands. **Flowers** are cream to yellow, about 2 cm across, comprising many stamens spreading from a central disc, and covered by a hemispherical beaked cap in bud, arranged in axillary clusters of 3-11 flowers on angular stalks to 15 mm long. **Buds** are urn-shaped with a pointed cap, wrinkled, to 17 mm long and 5 mm wide. **Fruits** are urn-shaped woody capsules with a broad base, on stout stalks, 8-10 mm long and 7-9 mm across with enclosed valves. **Flowering** mainly in winter and spring. **Habitat.** Widespread, mainly growing in sandy loams in southwestern WA and on the Eyre Peninsula in SA. **Family.** Myrtaceae.

Eucalyptus eximia — YELLOW BLOODWOOD

A small to medium-sized tree, 8-20 m high with an upright, often crooked trunk and a dense, well-branched or irregular broadly conical crown. **Bark** is yellow-brown, rough and flaky or scaly. **Mature leaves** are alternate, narrow lanceolate and slightly sickle-shaped, thick, 10-20 cm long and 10-25 mm wide on a flattened stalk 1-2 cm long, with a prominent midrib and parallel veins, dull grey-green above, paler below. **Flowers** are white to cream, about 3 cm across, comprising many stamens spreading from a central disc, and covered by a hemispherical to conical beaked cap in bud, arranged in terminal clusters of 5-7 flowers, stalkless or on short stalks. **Buds** are cylindrical to slightly conical, to 15 mm long and 8 mm across. **Fruits** are urn-shaped woody capsules, 13-20 mm long and 14-15 mm across, slightly ridged with enclosed valves. **Flowering** in spring. **Habitat.** Dry and well-drained slopes on sandy soils of the central coast of NSW. **Family.** Myrtaceae.

Eucalyptus gummifera — RED BLOODWOOD

A medium-sized to tall tree, 20-40 m high with a trunk to 1 m diameter, irregularly twisting branches and a well-developed crown. **Bark** is grey-brown, fibrous and flaky, tesselated, persistent, and often exudes a red gum. **Mature leaves** are alternate, lanceolate with a short stalk, prominent midrib and parallel veins, 10-16 cm long and 2-5 cm wide, dark green above, paler below. **Flowers** are cream to white, about 2 cm across, comprising many stamens spreading from a central disc, and covered by a hemispherical to conical or beaked cap in bud, arranged in 4-8 flowered clusters forming terminal racemes on flattened stalks 15-25 mm long. **Buds** are club-shaped, 8-12 mm long and 3-7 mm across. **Fruits** are urn-shaped woody capsules, 15-20 mm long and 11-18 mm across with 3 or 4 enclosed valves. **Flowering** in late summer and autumn. **Habitat.** Common in near coastal open moist forests at lower elevations in Qld, NSW and Vic. **Family.** Myrtaceae.

Eucalyptus flocktoniae

Eucalyptus eximia

Eucalyptus gummifera

Eucalyptus leucoxylon   YELLOW GUM. SOUTH AUSTRALIAN BLUE GUM

A small to medium-sized tree, 5-30 m high, well-formed with a straight trunk to 80 cm diameter on moister soils, spreading and stunted and crooked on poor sites. **Bark** is dark grey, rough and scaly at the base of the trunk, smooth, paler and often mottled with streaks of yellow, white and blue-grey higher up the trunk, shed in autumn revealing whitish new bark. **Mature leaves** are alternate, lanceolate with a prominent midrib and distinct veins, 7-20 cm long and 13-35 mm wide, deep olive or grey green, with a surface wax on new growth in inland populations. **Flowers** are cream, white or pink, about 3 cm across, comprising many stamens spreading from a central disc, and covered by a conical or hemispherical beaked cap in bud, arranged in clusters of 3 flowers on slender stalks to 1 cm long. **Buds** are ovoid to club-shaped, 6-15 mm long and 5-8 mm across. **Fruits** are cup or pear-shaped woody capsules, 7-12 mm across with 4-6 enclosed valves. **Flowering** in autumn, winter and spring. **Habitat.** Widely distributed in open forests and woodlands, preferring clay soils and higher rainfall areas on flat and hilly terrain in Vic. and SA. **Family.** Myrtaceae.

Eucalyptus maculata   SPOTTED GUM

A tall tree to 50 m high with a long, shaft-like trunk usually to 1.4 m diameter, and a fairly dense, high crown. **Bark** is smooth, conspicuously spotted with grey and yellow patches, and often dimpled. **Mature leaves** are alternate, lanceolate with a short stalk, prominent midrib and parallel lateral veins, dark green, often paler below, 10-30 cm long and 1-6 cm wide. **Flowers** are creamy-white, perfumed, about 2 cm across, comprising many stamens spreading from a central disc, and covered by a shortly pointed conical cap in bud, arranged in terminal clusters of usually 3 flowers. **Buds** are ovoid with a short point and usually with a reddish brown cap, 6-10 mm long and 4-6 mm across. **Fruits** are urn-shaped to ovoid woody capsules, 10-18 mm long and 9-12 mm across with 3-4 enclosed valves. **Flowering** in winter. **Habitat.** Widespread on sandy soils in taller open forests of the coast and up to 400 km inland in Qld, NSW and Vic. **Family.** Myrtaceae.

Eucalyptus calophylla   MARRI

A medium-sized to tall tree, 13-40 m high, with a thick trunk to 1.5 m diameter and a fairly dense heavily-branched spreading crown. **Bark** is grey becoming dark brown with age and frequently stained by reddish exuding kino, fibrous, rough and flaky with many small square scales, persistent to the small reddish branches. **Mature leaves** are alternate, broad lanceolate to ovate, 9-18 cm long and 20-45 mm wide on stalks to 2 cm long, glossy green above and paler below with a prominent midrib and parallel lateral veins. **Flowers** are pink or white, about 4 cm across, comprising many stamens spreading from a central disc, and covered by a hemispherical cap with a small point in bud, arranged in terminal clusters of 3-7 flowers. **Buds** are ovoid with a short point and a yellowish-green cap, 8-15 mm long and 5-9 mm across. **Fruits** are large urn-shaped woody capsules, 3-5 cm long and 3-4 cm across with 4 deeply enclosed valves and large black seeds to 2 cm long. **Flowering** in late summer and autumn. **Habitat.** Widespread on light sandy soils in open forests along the coast and nearby ranges in WA, but widely cultivated in eastern Australia. **Family.** Myrtaceae.

Eucalyptus leucoxylon

Eucalyptus maculata

M. Westmacott.

Eucalyptus calophylla

Eucalyptus woodwardii   LEMON-FLOWERED GUM

A small to medium-sized tree, 6-15 m high with a cylindrical trunk, sparse, somewhat pendulous branches, and an open crown. **Bark** is grey, smooth and shed in late summer and autumn to reveal pale pink new bark, streaked with large irregular patches of coppery-green. Older trees develop some persistent fibrous bark at the base; the young branchlets are glossy crimson beneath a whitish bloom. **Mature leaves** are alternate, lanceolate to sickle-shaped, thick and leathery, 10-15 cm long and 2-5 cm wide on stalks 2-3 cm long, pale green and covered with a bluish-grey bloom, with a prominent midrib and faint veins. **Flowers** are bright lemon-yellow and honey-scented, to 5 cm across, comprising many stamens spreading from a central disc, and covered by a pointed hemispherical cap in bud, arranged in axillary clusters of 3-7 flowers on stalks to 25 mm long. **Buds** are club-shaped, sometimes ridged and warted, covered with a powdery bloom, to 17 mm long and 1 cm wide. **Fruits** are conical to bell or urn-shaped woody capsules, yellowish-green with a whitish bloom, to 15 mm long with 5 triangular enclosed valves. **Flowering** in winter and spring. **Habitat.** Sandy soils in southern WA near the western edge of the Nullabor plain, cultivated as an ornamental. **Family.** Myrtaceae.

Eucalyptus ovata   SWAMP GUM

A small to medium-sized tree, 8-30 m high with a straight trunk to 1 m diameter, either with a fairly dense dark crown or poorly formed with sparse foliage at the ends of long branches. **Bark** is dark grey, hard and rough at the base, and shed in ribbons from the upper trunk and branches in summer and autumn, leaving a smooth grey to pink or yellow surface. **Mature leaves** are alternate, broad lanceolate to ovate, usually with broadly wavy margins, thick with a prominent midrib, 8-15 cm long and 2-5 cm wide, dark green and sometimes glossy. **Flowers** are white or cream, to 15 mm across, comprising many stamens spreading from a central disc, and covered by a hemispherical to conical cap in bud, arranged in axillary clusters of 4-8 (usually 7) flowers on stalks to 14 mm long. **Buds** are diamond-shaped to ovoid, green, 7-11 mm long and 4-6 mm across. **Fruits** are conical woody capsules, 5-7 mm across and 4-8 mm long with 3 or 4 barely enclosed valves. **Flowering** in autumn and winter. **Habitat.** Widespread and common on poorly drained and periodically swampy sites in open forests of the coast and tablelands in NSW, Vic., SA and Tas. **Family.** Myrtaceae.

Eucalyptus papuana   GHOST GUM

A small to medium-sized tree, 5-25 m high generally with a short straight trunk to 1 m diameter, dividing early into several large spreading branches producing a fairly tufted crown. **Bark** is light grey to white and smooth, sometimes with persistent scaly bark at the base of the trunk. **Mature leaves** are alternate, narrow to broad lanceolate, sometimes with wavy margins, 5-20 cm long and 10-35 mm wide. **Flowers** are creamy-white to greenish, about 15 mm across, comprising many stamens spreading from a central disc, and covered by a hemispherical to blunt conical cap in bud, arranged in short axillary clusters of 3-7 flowers on stalks 1-2 cm long. **Buds** are club-shaped, 5-7 mm long and 3-6 mm across. **Fruits** are conical to urn-shaped woody capsules, 6-11 mm across and 6-9 mm long with 3 enclosed valves. **Flowering** in spring and summer. **Habitat.** Widespread in undulating open country near watercourses and woodlands over much of northern Australia. **Family.** Myrtaceae.

Eucalyptus woodwardii

Eucalyptus ovata

Eucalyptus papuana

M.Westmacott

Eucalyptus robusta   SWAMP MAHOGANY

A medium-sized tree, 20-30 m high with a straight trunk to 1 m diameter, fairly dense spreading dark crown. **Bark** is red-brown, thick and rough, somewhat spongy and often flaky or fissured, persistent on the trunk and smaller branches. **Mature leaves** are alternate, broad lanceolate, tapering to a long fine point with a prominent midrib and parallel lateral veins, thick and leathery, glossy dark green above and paler below, 10-20 cm long and 3-8 cm wide. **Flowers** are creamy-white, to 25 mm across, comprising many stamens spreading from a central disc, and covered by a conical pointed cap in bud, arranged in dense axillary clusters of 5-15 flowers on flattened stalks 2-3 cm long. **Buds** are club-shaped with a long beak, 16-25 mm long and 4-8 mm across. **Fruits** are cylindrical to urn-shaped woody capsules, 12-18 mm long and 9-12 mm across with 3 or 4 enclosed valves with tips just protruding above rim level. **Flowering** mainly in spring and summer. **Habitat.** Coastal swamps and lagoons in Qld and NSW. **Family.** Myrtaceae.

Eucalyptus occidentalis   SWAMP OR FLAT-TOPPED YATE

A medium-sized tree, 10-20 m high with a straight trunk or a number of slender stems on poor sites, and a moderately dense flat-topped spreading crown. **Bark** is dark grey to black, rough and flaky with longitudinal furrows on the lower half of the tree and smooth grey-white on the upper parts, shedding in irregular strips at the junction of the two. **Mature leaves** are alternate, lanceolate, sometimes sickle-shaped, thick and leathery, 7-16 cm long and 2-3 cm wide on fairly long stalks, glossy green with a prominent midrib. **Flowers** are pale yellow, to 4 cm across, comprising many stamens spreading from a central disc, and covered by a finger-like cap 1-2 cm long in bud, on short thick stalks, arranged in axillary clusters of 3-8 flowers on flat stalks to 25 mm long. **Buds** are cylindrical to conical with long finger-like caps, 14-30 mm long and 5-6 mm wide. **Fruits** are cup-shaped to bell-shaped or urn-shaped faintly ribbed woody capsules, 8-15 mm long and 7-11 mm wide with 4 slender protruding valves. **Flowering** mainly in autumn and winter. **Habitat.** Woodlands in low-lying swamp-prone areas, often near salt lakes in southwestern WA. **Family.** Myrtaceae.

Eucalyptus saligna   SYDNEY BLUE GUM

A medium-sized to tall tree, 20-55 m high with a shaft-like trunk to 2.5 m diameter and a fairly sparse high elongated or spreading crown. **Bark** is grey to bluish-grey and smooth, peeling in long strips, with some persistent brown rough and flaky bark at the base of the trunk. **Mature leaves** are alternate, lanceolate, 9-20 cm long and 15-30 mm wide on stalks to 2 cm long, shiny dark green above and paler below with a prominent midrib and fine veins. **Flowers** are white, about 2 cm across, comprising many stamens spreading from a central disc, and covered by a pointed conical cap in bud, on flattened stalks, arranged in axillary clusters of 3-11 flowers on flattened or angular stalks about 2 cm long. **Buds** are ovoid to club-shaped, 6-9 mm long and 3-5 mm wide. **Fruits** are cup-shaped woody capsules, 5-8 mm long and 4-7 mm wide with 4 slightly protruding valves. **Flowering** in summer and autumn. **Habitat.** Common, preferring heavy deep soil in wet sclerophyll forests of the coast and lower slopes in southern Qld and NSW. **Family.** Myrtaceae.

Eucalyptus occidentalis

Eucalyptus robusta

Eucalyptus saligna

Eucalyptus punctata   GREY GUM

A medium-sized tree to 35 m high, sometimes gnarled and shrubby in exposed sites on poor soils, usually with a straight cylindrical trunk to 1 m diameter and a compact or spreading sparse crown. **Bark** is grey and dark grey, peeling in large patches to reveal cream to light orange new bark. **Mature leaves** are alternate, lanceolate, thick, 8-14 cm long and 2-3 cm wide on thin stalks, dark green above and paler below with a prominent midrib and fine veins. **Flowers** are white, about 1 cm across, comprising many stamens spreading from a central disc, and covered by a yellow-green narrow conical to beaked cap in bud, arranged in axillary clusters of 6-10 flowers on flattened stalks about 2 cm long. **Buds** are club-shaped, often ribbed, 7-16 mm long and 4-6 mm across. **Fruits** are conical to pear-shaped woody capsules, 5-12 mm across with 3-4 thick broad protruding valves. **Flowering** in summer. **Habitat.** Widespread, usually on sandy soils on well-drained ridges of the coast and lower tablelands in southern Qld and NSW. **Family.** Myrtaceae.

Eucalyptus macrocarpa   MOTTLECAH

A spreading mallee, 2-5 m high with a number of slender stems arising from an underground rootstock and a straggling crown of silvery-grey foliage. **Bark** is grey to light brown, smooth and shed to reveal light green new bark; the young branchlets are salmon-red. **Mature leaves** are variable, opposite to alternate, stalkless or stem-clasping, broad lanceolate to ovate or oblong, to 13 cm long and 8 cm wide, silvery grey with a prominent midrib. **Flowers** are large, red, pink or sometimes yellowish, 7-12 cm across, comprising many stamens spreading from a central disc, and covered by a large grey hemispherical to broadly conical pointed and slightly ribbed cap in bud, solitary or in pairs on very short stalks or stalkless. **Buds** are ovoid, about 5 cm long and 3-4 cm wide. **Fruits** are grey conical, flat-topped woody capsules, 7-9 cm across with long, narrow, centrally-protruding valves. **Flowering** most of the year, but mainly in winter and spring. **Habitat.** Open sandheaths in small stands between Hill River and Corrigan in southwestern WA, but widely cultivated. **Family.** Myrtaceae.

Eucalyptus oleosa   OIL OR ACORN MALLEE

A mallee or small spreading tree, 3-12 m high, often with a number of slender stems arising from an underground woody rootstock, and an open umbrella-like crown. **Bark** is grey to brownish-grey, smooth with rough fibrous darker deciduous bark at the base of the tree. **Mature leaves** are alternate, narrow lanceolate with a prominent midrib, faint veins and many oil glands, 5-12 cm long and 8-20 mm wide with stalks 8-18 mm long, shiny dark green or glaucous blue-green. **Flowers** are creamy-white to pale yellow, about 1 cm across, comprising many stamens spreading from a central disc, and covered by a blunt conical or domed cap in bud, arranged in clusters of 4-11 flowers on slightly flattened stalks to 1 cm long. **Buds** are acorn-like, 6-8 mm long and 3-4 mm across. **Fruits** are conical to pear-shaped woody capsules, 4-7 mm across with usually 3 fragile, needle-like protruding valves. **Flowering** mainly in winter and spring. **Habitat.** Widely distributed in open scrub regions on sandy soils in drier temperate regions of NSW, Vic., SA and WA. **Family.** Myrtaceae.

Eucalyptus punctata

Eucalyptus macrocarpa

Eucalyptus oleosa

Eucalyptus salmonophloia
SALMON GUM
A medium-sized tree to 30 m high with a straight trunk to 60 cm diameter and a moderately dense flattish spreading crown. **Bark** is pale grey, shed seasonally in large patches revealing light reddish-brown smooth new bark, turning salmon pink and weathering to grey. **Mature leaves** are alternate, narrow lanceolate, sometimes sickle-shaped, 6-12 cm long and 6-15 mm wide on narrow stalks, glossy green with a prominent midrib. **Flowers** are creamy-white, about 12 mm across, comprising many stamens spreading from a central disc, and covered by a rounded conical cap in bud, on stalks 2-5 mm long, arranged in axillary clusters of 7-13 flowers on slender stalks to 1 cm long. **Buds** are green, ovoid to globular, 3-7 mm long and 3-5 mm wide. **Fruits** are pear-shaped woody capsules, 3-5 mm across with 3 slender pointed protruding valves. **Flowering** in summer and autumn. **Habitat.** Widespread in open forests and woodlands, inland on various soils in southwestern WA. **Family.** Myrtaceae.

Eucalyptus grandis
FLOODED OR ROSE GUM
A tall tree to 55 m high with a long straight trunk to 3 m diameter, ascending branches usually high in the tree and a tufted, fairly sparse crown in forest sites, dense and conical in open areas. **Bark** is white to light grey, smooth, generally with some flaky rough black bark near the base of the trunk. **Mature leaves** are alternate, lanceolate with a prominent midrib and often with wavy margins, 10-20 cm long and 20-35 mm wide on a stalk about 2 cm long, shiny dark green above and paler below. **Flowers** are white, about 2 cm across, comprising many stamens spreading from a central disc, and covered by a conical, somewhat beaked cap in bud, arranged in axillary clusters of 3-12 flowers on a flattened stalk about 2 cm long. **Buds** are yellowish-green, club-shaped, 5-8 mm long and 3-4 mm across. **Fruits** are pear-shaped stalkless woody capsules, 6-8 mm long with 4-5 protruding valves. **Flowering** in winter. **Habitat.** Wet sclerophyll forests on moist, well-drained soils of higher fertility in coastal Qld and NSW. **Family.** Myrtaceae.

Eucalyptus eremophila
TALL SAND MALLEE
A mallee or small tree to 8 m high usually with a number of slender stems arising from an underground woody stock, and a dense crown of stiff foliage. **Bark** is light grey or brown, polished and smooth, peeling in late summer to reveal yellowish-brown new bark. **Mature leaves** are alternate, lanceolate with a flattened stalk, 6-12 cm long and 1-2 cm wide, fleshy, grey-green to blue-green with a prominent midrib. **Flowers** are cream to bright yellow, rarely dull red, about 3 cm across, comprising many stamens spreading from a central disc, and covered by a very long curved and pointed reddish cap in bud, arranged in drooping axillary clusters of 3-7 flowers on a slightly flattened stalk to 25 mm long. **Buds** are finger-like with a hemispherical calyx tube and a long narrow horn-shaped cap, 5-6 cm long. **Fruits** are pear-shaped woody capsules, 10-12 mm long and 8-10 mm across with enclosed or slightly protruding valves. **Flowering** in winter and spring. **Habitat.** Widespread in semi-arid areas, preferring sandy soils, in southwestern WA, widely planted as an ornamental. **Family.** Myrtaceae.

Eucalyptus
salmonophloia

Eucalyptus grandis

Eucalyptus eremophila

Eucalyptus radiata   NARROW-LEAVED PEPPERMINT

A small to tall tree 10-50 m high with a straight trunk to 1.5 m diameter and a fairly dense, fine-textured crown. **Bark** is closely fibrous, dark grey to brown, rough and persistent, often covered with lichen, smooth and whitish on the branchlets. **Mature leaves** are alternate, narrow lanceolate with a stalk and prominent midrib, thin, dull green with numerous oil glands giving a strong peppermint taste and smell, 8-16 cm long and 8-28 mm wide. **Flowers** are white to cream, about 15 mm across, comprising many stamens spreading from a central disc, and covered by a conical to hemispherical cap in bud, arranged in axillary clusters of 7-16 flowers on long stalks. **Buds** are club-shaped, 3-6 mm long and 2-4 mm across. **Fruits** are cup-shaped or pear-shaped woody capsules, 4-6 mm diameter with 3-4 valves at or below rim level. **Flowering** in spring and summer. **Habitat.** Common and widespread along the foothills and tablelands up to 1200 m in eastern and southeastern Vic and NSW. **Family.** Myrtaceae.

Eucalyptus populnea   BIMBLE BOX. POPLAR GUM

A small to medium tree 10-25 m high with a poorly formed or tall straight trunk to 80 cm diameter, usually low-branching giving a fairly large spreading or rounded and dense crown. **Bark** is closely fibrous or scaly, light grey to brown and persistent. **Mature leaves** are alternate, broad lanceolate to ovate with long slender stalks and prominent midrib, glossy green, 5-11 cm long and 15-30 mm wide. **Flowers** are white, about 8 mm across, comprising many stamens spreading from a central disc, and covered by a hemispherical or conical cap in bud, arranged in axillary clusters of 4-15 flowers forming small terminal panicles on stalks about 1 cm long. **Buds** are club-shaped, 3-5 mm long and 2-3 mm across. **Fruits** are pear-shaped to conical woody capsules, 2-5 mm diameter with usually 4 small barely enclosed valves. **Flowering** in summer and autumn. **Habitat.** Common in open woodlands of the flatter inland areas of central eastern Qld and NSW. **Family.** Myrtaceae.

Eucalyptus polyanthemos   RED BOX

A small to medium tree 7-25 m high, often crooked in form with a trunk to 1 m diameter, usually with a fairly dense spreading or rounded greyish crown. **Bark** is closely fibrous or scaly, grey, persistent to the small branches, often rough, but sometimes shed in irregular flakes or strips leaving a smooth mottled grey, pink and cream surface. **Mature leaves** are alternate, broad lanceolate to ovate or elliptical with long slender stalks and prominent midrib, grey-green, 5-10 cm long and 15-50 mm wide. **Flowers** are white, cream or pinkish, about 12 mm across, comprising many stamens spreading from a central disc, and covered by a hemispherical to conical cap narrower than the top of the calyx tube in bud, arranged in clusters of 3-7 flowers forming terminal panicles on stalks about 1 cm long. **Buds** are club-shaped, 5-6 mm long and 2-4 mm across. **Fruits** are pear-shaped woody capsules, 4-7 mm diameter with usually 4 enclosed valves and depressed disc. **Flowering** in spring and summer. **Habitat.** Common in drier open forests in the lowlands and lower ranges of central and eastern Vic. and southern NSW. **Family.** Myrtaceae.

Eucalyptus radiata

Eucalyptus populnea

Eucalyptus polyanthemos

Eucalyptus annulata   OPEN-FRUITED MALLEE

A mallee or small tree, 3-8 m high with a single trunk or a number of slender stems arising from an underground woody rootstock, and a wide spreading crown of moderately dense foliage. **Bark** is grey to greyish-brown, smooth and peeling in late summer to reveal yellowish-brown or yellowish-green new bark; young branchlets are reddish-purple. **Mature leaves** are alternate, narrow lanceolate, sometimes sickle-shaped, often with a curved pointed tip, 7-13 cm long and 1-2 cm wide, glossy dark green with a prominent midrib and faint veins. **Flowers** are creamy-yellow, about 25 mm across on flattened stalks, comprising many stamens spreading from a central disc, and covered by a cylindrical pointed often red cap in bud, arranged in axillary clusters of 6-12 flowers. **Buds** are cylindrical to club-shaped, 16-23 mm long and 6-7 mm across. **Fruits** are reddish-brown cup-shaped woody stalkless capsules, about 12 mm long and 7 mm across with sharply pointed protruding valves. **Flowering** in winter and spring. **Habitat.** Often forms large copses on clay or gravelly soils in drier areas of southwestern WA. **Family.** Myrtaceae.

Eucalyptus foecunda   NARROW-LEAVED RED MALLEE

A mallee or small tree, 2-8 m high, usually with a number of slender stems arising from an underground woody rootstock, and an open umbrella-like crown. **Bark** is pale grey, smooth and shed in ribbons to reveal reddish-brown fresh bark. **Mature leaves** are alternate, narrow lanceolate with a prominent midrib, 3-9 cm long and 4-9 mm wide with stalks 5-10 mm long, thick and shiny green, dotted with glands. **Flowers** are creamy-white, to 15 mm across, comprising many stamens spreading from a central disc, and covered by a conical cap in bud, arranged in axillary clusters of 3-13 flowers crowded near the ends of the branchlets on stalks about 1 cm long. **Buds** are ovoid, often with more than one generation present simultaneously, usually reddish, 6-8 mm long and 3-4 mm across. **Fruits** are cup or pear-shaped woody capsules with a thick, flattened rim, 3-6 mm across with 3-4 fragile, needle-like protruding valves. **Flowering** in summer and autumn. **Habitat.** Widely distributed in mallee scrub regions on sandy soils, sometimes near salt lakes in central NSW, Vic., SA and WA. **Family.** Myrtaceae.

Eucalyptus diversifolia   SOAP OR SOUTH AUSTRALIAN COAST MALLEE

A mallee or small tree, 3-10 m high with a single trunk in favourable sites or with a number of slender stems arising from an underground woody rootstock, and a wide spreading crown. **Bark** is light to dark grey and smooth, peeling in long strips in late summer and autumn to reveal pale grey new bark. **Mature leaves** are alternate, lanceolate, 5-12 cm long and 1-2 cm wide on stalks 8-20 mm long, thick, dull green with a prominent midrib and faint veins. **Flowers** are white to cream, fragrant, about 15 mm across, comprising many stamens spreading from a central disc, and covered by a conical to hemispherical pointed cap in bud, arranged in axillary clusters of 4-11 flowers. **Buds** are club-shaped, 7-10 mm long and 5-6 mm across. **Fruits** are reddish-brown cup-shaped woody capsules with a raised rim, 8-15 mm across with 3-4 enclosed valves. **Flowering** in winter and spring. **Habitat.** Common in open scrubs with other mallees along the coast of southwestern Vic., SA and southern WA. **Family.** Myrtaceae.

Eucalyptus annulata

Eucalyptus foecunda

Eucalyptus diversifolia

M. Westmacott

Eucalyptus salubris. GIMLET

A small to medium-sized tree, 6-25 m high with a straight trunk to 60 cm diameter, steeply-angled limbs beginning half-way up the tree or at ground level, and a moderately dense crown at the ends of the branches. **Bark** is red-brown weathering to grey-brown, smooth, shiny and spirally fluted, particularly in young trees, shed in ribbons in late summer revealing light brown new bark. **Mature leaves** are alternate, narrow lanceolate with a prominent midrib, 5-10 cm long and 8-13 mm wide, glossy green on stalks 8-15 mm long. **Flowers** are cream, about 2 cm long, comprising many stamens spreading from a central disc, and covered by a rounded conical cap in bud, arranged in axillary clusters of 7 flowers on flattened stalks to 1 cm long. **Buds** are ovoid, 7-12 mm long and 3-5 mm across. **Fruits** are cup-shaped woody capsules, 3-6 mm long and 5-8 mm across with 3 or 4 protruding valves. **Flowering** mainly in summer and autumn. **Habitat.** Widespread in flat low woodlands, often in pure stands inland in southwestern WA. **Family.** Myrtaceae.

Eucalyptus tessellaris CARBEEN. MORETON BAY ASH

A small to medium-sized tree, 10-35 m high with a straight trunk to 1 m diameter, with a rounded or spreading, fairly sparse crown of slender branches and drooping branchlets. **Bark** is dark grey, rough, tesselated and persistent at the base of the trunk, smooth and light grey on the upper trunk. **Mature leaves** are alternate, narrow lanceolate to sickle-shaped with a prominent midrib, 6-20 cm long and 7-20 mm wide, dull greyish-green. **Flowers** are cream to white, about 15 mm long, comprising many stamens spreading from a central disc, and covered by a flatly conical or beret-shaped cap in bud, arranged in globular clusters of 2-7 flowers on very short angular stalks forming terminal panicles. **Buds** are ovoid to pear-shaped, 4-8 mm long and 3-5 mm across. **Fruits** are cup to urn-shaped, thin-walled woody capsules, 5-12 mm long and 5-9 mm across with 3 enclosed valves. **Flowering** in summer. **Habitat.** Widespread in forests and open woodlands, preferring deep sandy soils near watercourses in northeastern NSW and eastern Qld. **Family.** Myrtaceae.

Eucalyptus microcorys TALLOW-WOOD

A large tree to 60 m high with a long straight trunk to 3 m diameter and an irregular open crown. **Bark** is red-brown, rough and persistent to the small branches, soft, fibrous, deeply furrowed with corky patches **Mature leaves** are alternate, broad lanceolate with a sharp point, thin with a prominent midrib, 7-13 cm long and 15-35 mm wide on stalks to 2 cm long, glossy green above and paler below. **Flowers** are white or cream, about 15 mm across, comprising many stamens spreading from a central disc, and covered by a hemispherical cap in bud, arranged in clusters of 4-7 flowers. **Buds** are club-shaped, 4-6 mm long and 2-3 mm across. **Fruits** are cup-shaped to conical woody capsules sometimes with faint ribs, 4-10 mm long and 3-6 mm across with 3 slightly protruding or enclosed valves. **Flowering** in winter, spring and early summer. **Habitat.** Widespread in hilly country in open forests and rainforest margins of the coast and adjacent ranges in Qld and NSW. **Family.** Myrtaceae.

Eucalyptus salubris

Eucalyptus tessellaris

Eucalyptus microcorys

M. Westmacott

Eucalyptus botryoides   BANGALAY. SOUTHERN MAHOGANY

A medium to tall tree, 10-40 m high with a straight trunk to 1 m diameter, usually with long ascending, spreading branches forming a fairly dense crown. On exposed coastal sites may be reduced to a heavily branched shrubby tree. **Bark** is dark brown, fibrous, thick and soft, and often fissured on the trunk and lower branches, smooth and grey to pale brown on smaller branches. **Mature leaves** are alternate, broad lanceolate, often tapering to a long fine point, with a prominent midrib and many fine lateral veins, glossy dark green above, paler below, thick, 10-16 cm long and 3-6 cm wide. **Flowers** are cream or white, about 2 cm across, comprising many stamens spreading from a central disc, and covered by a hemispherical to conical cap in bud, arranged in axillary clusters of 7-11 flowers on broad flattened stalks to 15 mm long. **Buds** are cylindrical to club-shaped and ribbed, to 9 mm long and 6 mm across. **Fruits** are cup-shaped woody capsules, 7-12 mm long and 5-9 mm across, sometimes slightly ribbed, with 3 or 4 enclosed valves. **Flowering** in summer. **Habitat.** Near-coastal forests, often on sand dunes and in river valleys at low altitudes in NSW and Vic. **Family.** Myrtaceae.

Eucalyptus largiflorens   BLACK OR RIVER BOX

A small to medium-sized tree, 10-25 m high with a short trunk to 1 m diameter, often poorly formed with low, widely spreading and irregularly shaped branches and a rounded or spreading crown. **Bark** is rough, closely fissured or scaly, dark grey to black, persistent or sometimes shed from the upper branches leaving a smooth white surface. **Mature leaves** are alternate, narrow lanceolate, often with a curved tip, pointed, with a prominent midrib and faint veins, dull greyish green, thick, 6-18 cm long and 1-2 cm wide. **Flowers** are pink or cream, about 1 cm across, comprising many stamens spreading from a central disc, and covered by a hemispherical to conical cap in bud, arranged in clusters of 3-7 flowers forming axillary or terminal panicles on stalks about 1 cm long. **Buds** are club-shaped, usually with faint ribs, 3-5 mm long and 2-3 mm across. **Fruits** are cup-shaped woody capsules, 3-6 mm long and 3-5 mm across with 3 or 4 tiny enclosed valves. **Flowering** in spring and summer. **Habitat.** Widespread throughout the dry central plains near water courses, often in pure stands of open woodlands in Qld, NSW, Vic. and SA. **Family.** Myrtaceae.

Eucalyptus obliqua   MESSMATE. MESSMATE STRINGYBARK

A medium to tall tree, 13-70 m high with a straight trunk 1-3 m diameter and moderately dense crown, may be reduced to a tall shrub on exposed poor sites. **Bark** is rough, thick, coarsely fibrous and stringy, grey on the surface but red-brown beneath. **Mature leaves** are alternate, broad lanceolate or sickle-shaped with an asymmetrical base and prominent midrib and distinct lateral veins, glossy dark green, thick, 9-16 cm long and 15-33 mm wide. **Flowers** are white or cream, about 15 mm across, comprising many stamens spreading from a central disc, and covered by a hemispherical to conical cap in bud, arranged in axillary clusters of 7-15 flowers on angular or flattened stalks to 15 mm long. **Buds** are club-shaped, 6-7 mm long and 3-4 mm across. **Fruits** are cup-shaped to urn-shaped woody capsules, 6-11 mm long and 5-9 mm across with 3 or 4 enclosed valves. **Flowering** in summer. **Habitat.** Common and widespread in moister open forests on the foothills and tablelands to about 1300 m, mainly in Vic. and Tas., to a lesser extent in Qld, NSW and SA. **Family.** Myrtaceae.

Eucalyptus botryoides

Eucalyptus largiflorens

Eucalyptus obliqua

Eucalyptus rossii   WHITE OR SCRIBBLY GUM

Usually a crooked or gnarled tree with irregular branches on poorer sites to 15 m high, taller and more shapely on richer soils to 25 m high, with a trunk diameter of up to 1 m and fairly open spreading crown. **Bark** is smooth and shed in flakes, yellow at first, weathering to grey, often mottled, commonly with brown scribbly markings due to insect larvae. **Mature leaves** are alternate, narrow lanceolate to sickle-shaped with a short stalk and prominent midrib, 7-17 cm long and 6-15 mm wide, dull green, often greyish. **Flowers** are creamy-white, about 15 mm across, comprising many stamens spreading from a central disc, and covered by a hemispherical to conical cap in bud, arranged in axillary clusters of 5-15 flowers on stalks about 1 cm long. **Buds** are club-shaped, 4-7 mm long and 2-3 mm across. **Fruits** are ovoid woody capsules, 4-5 mm long and 5-6 mm across with usually 4 valves at about rim level on a flat or convex disc. **Flowering** in summer. **Habitat.** Naturally occurring in open forests and woodlands, usually on dry soils on hillsides and ridges up to 1000 m in NSW. **Family.** Myrtaceae.

Eucalyptus camaldulensis   RIVER RED GUM

A medium-sized to tall tree, 15-50 m high with a short thick trunk, 1-2 m or occasionally 4 m diameter, heavy twisting branches and large spreading crown. **Bark** is dull white usually blotched with creamy-yellow or red, smooth and shed in irregular flakes. **Mature leaves** are alternate, lanceolate with a short stalk and prominent midrib, 8-25 cm long and 7-20 mm wide, dull green, often greyish. **Flowers** are creamy-white, about 15 mm across, comprising many stamens spreading from a central disc, and covered by a hemispherical to pointed conical cap in bud, arranged in axillary clusters of 5-11 flowers on slender stalks 2-5 cm long. **Buds** are more or less globular, contracting to a point, 5-11 mm long and 3-5 mm across. **Fruits** are ovoid woody capsules, 3-6 mm long and 5-10 mm across with usually 4 strongly projecting valves. **Flowering** in spring and summer. **Habitat.** Widespread in open forests and woodlands, usually along inland watercourses and floodplains at low elevations in all mainland states. **Family.** Myrtaceae.

Eucalyptus pauciflora   SNOW GUM. WHITE SALLEE

A medium-sized, often crooked tree usually to 20 m high with a short trunk to 1 m diameter, low branching with a spreading, open crown. **Bark** is shed in irregular patches in autumn, leaving a smooth white to yellow, olive-green or brown surface, occasionally with scribbly markings from insect larvae. **Mature leaves** are alternate, variable, lanceolate to sickle-shaped or even ovate, with a short stalk, prominent midrib and almost parallel longitudinal veins, 6-19 cm long and 15-30 mm wide, thick, leathery and shiny green. **Flowers** are white or cream, about 15 mm across, comprising many stamens spreading from a central disc, and covered by a hemispherical to conical cap with a short point in bud, arranged in axillary clusters of 7-15 flowers on thick stalks to 16 mm long. **Buds** are club-shaped, 5-15 mm long and 3-6 mm across. **Fruits** are ovoid to cup-shaped woody capsules, 7-14 mm across with 3 or 4 valves at rim level. **Flowering** in spring and early summer. **Habitat.** Widely distributed in open forests and woodlands, particularly above 1200 m, scattered in the lowlands of NSW, Vic., SA and Tas. **Family.** Myrtaceae.

Eucalyptus rossii

Eucalyptus camaldulensis

Eucalyptus pauciflora

Eucalyptus microcarpa   GREY OR NARROW-LEAVED BOX

A medium-sized tree usually to 25 m high with a straight trunk to 1 m diameter, long ascending branches form a large, moderately dense crown. **Bark** is grey, scaly or shortly-fibrous on the trunk and larger branches, paler and smooth on smaller branches. **Mature leaves** are alternate, lanceolate with a short stalk and prominent midrib, thick, green or grey green, 8-15 cm long and 10-25 mm wide. **Flowers** are creamy-white, about 15 mm across, comprising many stamens spreading from a central disc, and covered by a conical cap in bud, arranged in terminal or axillary clusters of 4-8 flowers. **Buds** are ovoid, often with ridges and bent tips, 3-9 mm long and 2-4 mm across. **Fruits** are ovoid to cup-shaped woody capsules, 3-7 mm long and 3-5 mm across usually with 4 enclosed valves. **Flowering** in late summer, autumn and winter. **Habitat.** Widespread on inland slopes and plains on dry creek beds and in woodlands to 400m in Qld, NSW, Vic. and SA. **Family.** Myrtaceae.

Eucalyptus sideroxylon   RED IRONBARK. MUGGA

A medium-sized tree, 10-30 m high with a trunk to about 1 m diameter, often crooked and dividing near the base, and a high, medium-density crown. **Bark** is dark grey to brown or black, hard, thick, rough and deeply furrowed, persistent to the smaller branches, and impregnated with red kino. **Mature leaves** are alternate, lanceolate with a prominent midrib and faint veins, 6-14 cm long and 10-30 mm wide, dull dark green or greyish blue. **Flowers** are cream, white or pink, 15-20 mm across, comprising many stamens spreading from a central disc, and covered by a pointed conical cap in bud, arranged in axillary clusters of 3-9 flowers on stalks 15-20 mm long. **Buds** are ovoid to club-shaped, 7-12 mm long and 4-8 mm across. **Fruits** are ovoid to pear-shaped woody capsules, 5-14 mm across with 5 or 6 enclosed valves. **Flowering** in winter and spring. **Habitat.** Drier open forests or woodlands on well-drained poor, shallow soils on low ridges or undulating terrain below 550 m in Qld, NSW and Vic. **Family.** Myrtaceae.

Eucalyptus gracilis   YORREL. WHITE MALLEE

A mallee or small tree, 3-18 m high with a single trunk or a number of slender stems arising from a woody rootstock, and a spreading crown with moderately dense pendulous foliage. **Bark** is dark grey and rough at the base of the trunk, pale grey and smooth on the upper parts, shed in autumn to reveal red-brown new bark. **Mature leaves** are alternate, narrow lanceolate, 4-9 cm long and 5-15 mm wide on stalks 4-15 mm long, glossy green with a prominent midrib and conspicuous oil glands. **Flowers** are white, 1 cm across, comprising many stamens spreading from a central disc, and covered by a hemispherical to conical cap with a tiny point in bud, arranged in axillary clusters of 3-7 flowers on flattened stalks to 1 cm long. **Buds** are club-shaped, 4-5 mm long and 3-4 mm wide. **Fruits** are ovoid to pear-shaped woody capsules with thin walls and a narrow rim, 4-6 mm long and 3-5 mm across with deeply enclosed small valves. **Flowering** in autumn, winter and spring. **Habitat.** Widespread and common in mallee scrubs on sandy soils in NSW, Vic., SA and WA. **Family.** Myrtaceae.

Eucalyptus microcarpa

Eucalyptus sideroxylon

Eucalyptus gracilis

M.Westmacott

Eucalyptus blakelyi   BLAKELY'S RED GUM

A medium-sized tree to 25 m high with a stout trunk to about 1 m diameter, soon dividing into large ascending branches to form a broad, rounded and somewhat conical crown with pendulous branchlets. **Bark** is grey and smooth, shed in large irregular patches revealing creamy-yellow, white, grey or bluish new bark. **Mature leaves** are alternate, lanceolate or slightly sickle-shaped, 9-20 cm long and 1-3 cm wide on stalks to 35 mm long, dark green to slightly grey with a prominent midrib and faint veins. **Flowers** are white or pink, about 15 mm across, comprising many stamens spreading from a central disc, and covered by a slender reddish conical to horn-shaped cap in bud, arranged in axillary clusters of 5-11 flowers on a slightly flattened stalk 7-19 mm long. **Buds** are 6-14 mm long and 3-6 mm wide with an obconical calyx tube about half the length of the cap. **Fruits** are ovoid woody capsules, 3-8 mm across with 3-4 protruding pointed valves. **Flowering** in spring and early summer. **Habitat.** Widespread in open forests and woodlands, preferring compact loamy soils on undulating terrain of the lower inland slopes of the eastern tablelands in southern Qld, NSW and Vic. **Family.** Myrtaceae.

Eucalyptus lehmannii   BUSHY YATE

A mallee or small tree to 10 m high with a short twisted trunk or a number of slender stems arising from a woody rootstock, and a compact rounded and spreading or irregular crown with very low branches. **Bark** is reddish-brown, often rough at the base and fissured or scaly. **Mature leaves** are alternate, ovate to obovate, thick and leathery, 7-10 cm long and 2-3 cm wide on short stalks with a prominent midrib. **Flowers** are pale yellow to greenish-white, comprising many stamens spreading from a central disc, and covered by a finger-like cap 3-5 cm long in bud, stalkless, they are arranged in axillary globular clusters to about 12 cm across of 7-15 flowers fused together on a common flattened stalk about 1 cm wide. **Buds** are fused into a globular cluster with the long finger-like reddish caps protruding from the fused discs. **Fruits** are stalkless bell-shaped slightly ribbed woody capsules on a stout common stalk forming a globular cluster, 5-8 cm across, each with 4 long protruding pointed valves. **Flowering** in winter and spring. **Habitat.** Sandy soils along the coast of southwestern WA, commonly planted in streets and gardens. **Family.** Myrtaceae.

Eucalyptus microtheca   COOLIBAH

A small to medium-sized tree to 20 m high usually with a short, often slightly crooked trunk to 1 m diameter and a fairly open crown; small and poorly formed with a straggly crown and very short trunk in poor situations. **Bark** is grey to black, short-fibred, flaky and persistent to the larger branches, becoming deeply furrowed at the base, the upper bark is smooth and white or pale grey. Sometimes the bark peels completely leaving a smooth white surface. **Mature leaves** are alternate, lanceolate, 7-17 cm long and 8-25 mm wide, green to greyish-green with a prominent midrib. **Flowers** are white to cream, rarely pink, comprising many stamens spreading from a central disc, and covered by a hemispherical cap in bud, arranged in terminal panicles of 3-7 flowers on a thin stalk 3-10 mm long. **Buds** are ovoid, 3-5 mm long and 2-3 mm wide. **Fruits** are small ovoid to hemispherical woody capsules, 3-7 mm across with 3-4 broad protruding valves. **Flowering** in summer. **Habitat.** Widespread in arid and semi-arid areas near watercourses and seasonally inundated areas in open woodlands, to about 700 m in all states except Vic. and Tas. **Family.** Myrtaceae.

Eucalyptus blakelyi

Eucalyptus lehmannii

Eucalyptus microtheca

Eucalyptus pilularis   BLACKBUTT

A tall tree to 65 m high with a long straight cylindrical trunk to 3 m diameter and a fairly open elongated to spreading crown. **Bark** is greyish-brown, rough and fibrous, shedding in strips from the upper trunk leaving a smooth white or yellowish-grey surface often with scribbly insect markings. **Mature leaves** are alternate, lanceolate to sickle-shaped, 9-16 cm long and 16-40 mm wide, dark glossy green above and slightly paler below with a prominent midrib. **Flowers** are white, about 15 mm across, comprising many stamens spreading from a central disc, and covered by a pointed conical cap in bud, arranged in axillary clusters of 7-15 flowers on flattened stalks about 15 mm long. **Buds** are club-shaped, 8-11 mm long and 4-5 mm across, smooth or with 2 ribs. **Fruits** are hemispherical to globular woody capsules, 8-12 mm across with 4 small enclosed valves. **Flowering** in spring, summer and autumn. **Habitat.** Common along the coast and lower slopes to 300 m high usually in tall open forests on soils of moderate fertility in Qld and NSW. **Family.** Myrtaceae.

Eucalyptus intertexta   GUM-BARKED COOLIBAH

A mallee to medium-sized tree, 5-30 m high, erect or crooked with a trunk to about 1 m diameter, occasionally with several slender stems, and a sparse crown. **Bark** is grey to red-brown, rough, thick and scaly to fibrous at the base of the trunk, shedding to become smooth with various pale shades of grey, brown and green higher up. **Mature leaves** are alternate, broad to narrow lanceolate with a prominent midrib and a faint marginal vein near the leaf edge, 6-14 cm long and 10-25 mm wide, dull greyish-green, thick and leathery. **Flowers** are cream or white, about 1 cm across, comprising many stamens spreading from a central disc, and covered by a conical or hemispherical cap in bud, in clusters of 4-7 flowers arranged in terminal panicles on stalks 8-12 mm long. **Buds** are ovoid to club-shaped, sometimes faintly ribbed, 3-9 mm long and 2-4 mm across. **Fruits** are ovoid to pear-shaped woody capsules, 4-7 mm across with 4 or 5 enclosed valves. **Flowering** in autumn and winter. **Habitat.** Widespread in open woodlands on red-soil plains, often near dry watercourses or rocky rises, favouring well-drained soils in the central and south eastern inland areas of Qld, NSW, SA, WA and NT. **Family.** Myrtaceae.

Eucalyptus elata   RIVER PEPPERMINT

A small to tall tree, 7-45 m high with a slender trunk to 1 m diameter, fairly sparse foliage, slightly spreading or ascending branches and brown to reddish drooping branchlets. **Bark** is grey-brown to almost black, rough, fibrous and fissured on the lower trunk, peeling in long ribbons higher up to leave a smooth white surface. **Mature leaves** are alternate, narrow lanceolate with faint veins and prominent midrib, 10-22 cm long and 11-21 mm wide with numerous oil glands producing a strong peppermint taste and smell when crushed. **Flowers** are white or cream, about 15 mm across, comprising many stamens spreading from a central disc, and covered by a hemispherical to conical cap in bud, arranged in dense axillary clusters of 15-40 flowers on angular stalks to 1 cm long. **Buds** are club-shaped, 4-5 mm long and 2-3 mm across. **Fruits** are hemispherical to globular woody capsules, 4-6 mm across with 3 or 4 enclosed valves. **Flowering** mainly in spring and summer. **Habitat.** Near coastal open forests to 750 m on moist, well-drained soils in gullies and riversides in NSW and Vic. **Family.** Myrtaceae.

Eucalyptus pilularis

Eucalyptus intertexta

Eucalyptus elata

Eucalyptus crebra   NARROW-LEAVED RED IRONBARK
A medium-sized tree to 30 m high with a long straight trunk to 1.5 m diameter and
a fairly open, rather straggly crown, the lower branches beginning more than half
way up the trunk. **Bark** is light to dark grey or black, hard and deeply furrowed,
exuding a reddish gum in places, and persistent to the smaller branches. **Mature
leaves** are alternate, narrow lanceolate with a prominent midrib and thin stalk, 7-
16 cm long and 7-13 mm wide, dull green or grey-green. **Flowers** are cream or white,
about 12 mm across, comprising many stamens spreading from a central disc, and
covered by a conical or hemispherical cap in bud, arranged in terminal panicles of 4-
11 flowers on stalks about 1 cm long. **Buds** are diamond-shaped, 3-8 mm long and
2-4 mm across. **Fruits** are ovoid to pear-shaped woody capsules, 4-6 mm across
with 3-4 enclosed valves. **Flowering** in winter, spring and early summer. **Habitat.**
Widely distributed in open forests and woodlands on a wide variety of soils from the
coast to the edge of the western plains on low plateaux and undulating plains in Qld
and NSW. **Family.** Myrtaceae.

Eucalyptus marginata   JARRAH
A large tree to 40 m high with a straight trunk to 2 m diameter and a well-developed
crown of dark green foliage covering the top half of the tree; or it can be reduced to
a stunted mallee form on poor sites. **Bark** is red-brown when fresh, weathering to
grey, strong and fibrous with longitudinal fissures, rough and persistent to the
young branches. **Mature leaves** are alternate, lanceolate, tapering to a fine point,
with a prominent midrib, 8-13 cm long and 15-30 mm wide, glossy dark green
above and paler below. **Flowers** are creamy white, to 15 mm across, comprising
many stamens spreading from a central disc, and covered by a narrowly conical
reddish cap in bud, arranged in axillary clusters of 7-11 flowers on stalks to 2 cm
long. **Buds** are narrow and pointed, 8-17 mm long and 3-5 mm across. **Fruits** are
globular woody capsules, 9-16 mm across with 3 enclosed valves. **Flowering** in
spring and summer. **Habitat.** Common on sandy soils in southwestern WA.
Family. Myrtaceae.

Eucalyptus melliodora   YELLOW BOX
A medium-sized tree, 10-30 m high with a straight trunk to about 1 m diameter, with
a large rounded and spreading crown of medium density, with spreading or
ascending branches and drooping branchlets. **Bark** is grey to orange-brown or black,
rough and scaly or fibrous, shed in irregular strips in autumn to reveal whitish new
bark, the upper limbs are usually smooth and grey. **Mature leaves** are alternate,
lanceolate, thin with faint veins and prominent midrib, 6-14 cm long and 8-25 mm
wide, dull grey-green. **Flowers** are cream or rarely pink, perfumed, about 15 mm
across, comprising many stamens spreading from a central disc, and covered by a
hemispherical to conical cap in bud, arranged in axillary or terminal clusters of 3-7
flowers on stalks about 1 cm long. **Buds** are club-shaped, 5-8 mm long and 3-4 mm
across. **Fruits** are ovoid to cup-shaped woody capsules with a flat disc and distinct
stalk, 5-7 mm across and 4-7 mm long with usually 5 enclosed valves. **Flowering** in
spring and summer. **Habitat.** Widespread and common on better quality soils in
woodlands and open forests, mainly on the lower western slopes and tablelands in
Qld, NSW and Vic. **Family.** Myrtaceae.

Eucalyptus crebra

Eucalyptus marginata

Eucalyptus melliodora

Eucalyptus mannifera   RED-SPOTTED OR BRITTLE GUM

A small to medium-sized tree, 6-25 m high with an erect trunk (crooked in small varieties) and an open rounded or spreading crown of slender, pendulous leaves. **Bark** is white to cream or grey, smooth and powdery, becoming blue-grey to coppery red in summer before shedding in irregular ribbons and flakes. **Mature leaves** are alternate, narrow lanceolate to linear, slightly sickle-shaped, 6-15 cm long and 10-40 mm wide on stalks 1 cm long, with a prominent midrib and faint veins, bright green when young, becoming dull bluish-green. **Flowers** are cream to white, about 1 cm across, comprising many stamens spreading from a central disc, and covered by an elongated conical cap in bud, arranged in clusters of 4-7 flowers on stalks 4-6 mm long. **Buds** are broadly ovoid to spindle-shaped, 6-7 mm long. **Fruits** are spherical woody capsules, 4-6 mm across with 3-4 broad protruding valves. **Flowering** in spring and summer. **Habitat.** Common on poor shallow soils of the tablelands and foothills in southern NSW and Vic. **Family.** Myrtaceae.

Eucalyptus longicornis   RED MORRELL

A small to medium-sized tree, 8-30 m high with an upright cylindrical trunk to 60 cm diameter and a fairly spreading crown of medium density. **Bark** is grey, rough and finely fibrous on the trunk and lower branches, smooth and reddish on the upper branches. **Mature leaves** are alternate, narrow lanceolate, 7-12 cm long and 5-12 mm wide, glossy dark green with a prominent midrib. **Flowers** are white to cream, to 2 cm across, comprising numerous stamens spreading from a central disc, and covered by a reddish conical cap in bud, arranged in axillary clusters of 5-10 flowers on slender stalks about 1 cm long. **Buds** are club-shaped, about 1 cm long. **Fruits** are spherical to broadly pear-shaped woody capsules, 5-8 mm across with slender, protruding, pointed valves which easily fracture. **Flowering** mainly in late spring and summer. **Habitat.** Widespread on sandy soils and red or brown loams in the wheatbelt and goldfield areas of southwestern WA. **Family.** Myrtaceae.

Eucalyptus socialis   RED OR GREY MALLEE

A mallee or small tree, 2-12 m high, usually with a number of stems arising from an underground woody rootstock, and an open to moderately dense umbrella-like crown. **Bark** is dark grey, persistent and scaly at the base, shed in strips higher up in autumn to reveal white or yellowish new bark, smooth and grey to pale brown on the upper parts. **Mature leaves** are alternate, lanceolate, 6-14 cm long and 12-20 mm wide on stalks 1-2 cm long with oil glands, a prominent midrib and faint veins, dull, greyish-green with reddish new growth, leaves and twigs may be covered with a waxy bloom. **Flowers** are cream to white, about 2 cm across, comprising many stamens spreading from a central disc, and covered by an pointed conical cap in bud, arranged in axillary clusters of 4-15 flowers on flattened stalks to 2 cm long. **Buds** are somewhat cylindrical with a long conical cap, 8-13 mm long and 3-5 mm across. **Fruits** are spherical woody capsules, 5-8 mm across with 3-4 fragile, needle-like protruding valves. **Flowering** in spring and summer. **Habitat.** Commonly co-dominant in mallee scrub regions on sandy soils, usually on the plains of central NSW, Vic., SA, and WA. **Family.** Myrtaceae.

Eucalyptus mannifera

Eucalyptus longicornis

Eucalyptus socialis

M.Westmacott

Eucalyptus tereticornis   FOREST RED GUM

A medium-sized or tall tree, 20-50 m high with a straight trunk to 2 m diameter and fairly open elongated or spreading crown. **Bark** is mottled grey with irregular grey or bluish patches of various shades, shed in large flakes leaving a smooth surface and usually some persistent rough bark at the base. **Mature leaves** are alternate, narrow lanceolate to sickle-shaped with a stalk and prominent midrib, thick and glossy green, 8-20 cm long and 10-27 mm wide. **Flowers** are white, rarely pink, about 15 mm across, comprising many stamens spreading from a central disc, and covered by a long conical to horn-shaped cap in bud, arranged in axillary clusters of 5-12 flowers on stalks 15-25 mm long. **Buds** are spindle-shaped, 9-20 mm long and 3-5 mm across with a cap to 8 mm long. **Fruits** are ovoid woody capsules, 7-9 mm diameter with 4-5 protruding valves. **Flowering** in winter and spring. **Habitat.** Widespread along the coast and tablelands up to 1000 m in Qld, NSW and Vic. **Family.** Myrtaceae.

Eucalyptus macrorhyncha   RED STRINGYBARK

A medium-sized to tall tree, 15-35 m high with a straight trunk to 1 m diameter and a moderately dense and often rounded crown, although it is more straggly on poorer sites. **Bark** is dark grey-brown, rough and thick, usually deeply fissured with long stringy fibres, persistent to the smaller branches. **Mature leaves** are alternate, lanceolate with a stalk, prominent midrib and conspicuous veins, thick and dark green on both sides, 10-16 cm long and 12-30 mm wide. **Flowers** are white or cream, about 15 mm across, comprising many stamens spreading from a central disc, and covered by a smooth, tapering conical cap in bud, arranged in axillary clusters of 6-12 flowers. **Buds** are club-shaped, 9-15 mm long with angular or flattened stalks to 15 mm long. **Fruits** are spherical woody capsules, 9-12 mm diameter with 3 protruding valves. **Flowering** in summer and early autumn. **Habitat.** Widespread on drier, well-drained hilly sites in open forests to about 1000 m in NSW, Vic. and near Clare in SA. **Family.** Myrtaceae.

Eucalyptus viminalis   MANNA OR RIBBON GUM

Commonly a tall tree to 50 m high with a straight trunk to 1.5 m diameter and an open, elongated or spreading crown with drooping branches; but very variable in size and growth. **Bark** is smooth and white or cream, peeling in long ribbons during summer, with some rough, dark grey bark at the base. **Mature leaves** are alternate, narrow lanceolate to sickle-shaped with a prominent midrib, 10-20 cm long and 8-20 mm wide. **Flowers** are white, 15-20 mm across, comprising many stamens spreading from a central disc, and covered by a conical to hemispherical shortly-pointed cap in bud, arranged in axillary clusters of 3-7 flowers on flattened stalks 4-8 mm long. **Buds** are ovoid, stalkless, 7-10 mm long and 4-5 mm across. **Fruits** are spherical woody capsules, 5-9 mm diameter with 3-4 protruding valves, often arranged in threes with very short stalks. **Flowering** at any time but mainly in summer. **Habitat.** Widespread, mostly on moist soils near watercourses along the coast and tablelands up to 1400 m in southern Qld, NSW, Vic., SA and Tas. **Family.** Myrtaceae.

Eucalyptus tereticornis

Eucalyptus macrorhyncha

Eucalyptus viminalis

Eucalyptus pyriformis   PEAR-FRUITED MALLEE

A mallee or small tree, 2-6 m high, usually with a number of slender stems arising from an underground woody rootstock, and a wide straggling crown of moderately dense foliage. **Bark** is grey, smooth and peeling in strips during late summer and autumn to reveal pale brown new bark; the branchlets are angular and often reddish when young. **Mature leaves** are alternate, broad lanceolate to ovate, thick and glandular, 5-12 cm long and 15-40 mm wide, pale to mid-green with a prominent midrib and inconspicuous veins. **Flowers** are creamy-yellow, pink or red with yellow-tipped stamens, to 10 cm across on thick stalks, comprising many stamens spreading from a central disc, and covered by a hemispherical to conical ribbed pointed cap in bud, arranged in axillary clusters of 3 flowers on very thick stalks to 65 mm long. **Buds** are pear-shaped, ribbed, grey-green to reddish, 5-8 cm long and 30-38 mm across. **Fruits** are conical to hemispherical ribbed woody capsules, 4-7 cm long with barely enclosed valves. **Flowering** in winter and spring. **Habitat.** Well-drained sandy soils in southern WA and SA. **Family.** Myrtaceae.

Eucalyptus incrassata   YELLOW MALLEE

A mallee or small tree, 3-8 m high with a single trunk or a number of slender stems arising from a woody rootstock, and a spreading crown. **Bark** is pale grey to grey-brown, rough at the base of the trunk, peeling in strips in late summer to reveal smooth reddish new bark. **Mature leaves** are alternate, broad lanceolate, thick and leathery, 6-12 cm long and 14-30 mm wide on stalks 1-2 cm long, glossy pale green with a prominent midrib. **Flowers** are cream to white or rarely pink, about 2 cm across, comprising many stamens spreading from a central disc, and covered by a conical beaked reddish cap in bud, arranged in axillary clusters of 3-7 flowers on thick flattened stalks to 15 mm long. **Buds** are ribbed cylindrical to urn-shaped with a reddish conical cap, 12-22 mm long and 6-10 mm wide on very short stalks. **Fruits** are urn-shaped to cylindrical ribbed woody capsules, 10-12 mm long and 9-10 mm across with enclosed valves. **Flowering** in winter and spring. **Habitat.** Common in mallee scrubs on sandy soils in NSW, Vic., SA and WA. **Family.** Myrtaceae.

Eucalyptus globulus   SOUTHERN BLUE GUM

A medium-sized to tall tree, 15-70 m high with a stout trunk to 2 m diameter, and fairly spreading crown. **Bark** is grey-brown to almost black, rough and persistent at the base of the trunk, peeling in long strips in summer and autumn to leave a smooth surface in pale shades of grey, blue, cream or brown. **Mature leaves** are alternate, narrow lanceolate to sickle-shaped, pendulous, with fine, regular veins and prominent midrib, 12-30 cm long and 2-5 cm wide, thick, glossy dark green. **Flowers** are yellow to cream, comprising many stamens spreading from a central disc, and covered by a flattened cap with a pointed top in bud, solitary or in axillary clusters of 3-7 flowers, stalkless or on very short stalks. **Buds** are 4-angled, bluish-green, covered with a whitish bloom, warty, 15-30 mm long and 11-18 mm across. **Fruits** are conical to cup-shaped ribbed and warty woody capsules, 8-20 mm across with 3-5 enclosed or protruding valves and a broad usually convex disc. **Flowering** in spring and summer. **Habitat.** Scattered in moist hilly country in taller open forests along the coast and tablelands of NSW and Vic. **Family.** Myrtaceae.

Eucalyptus pyriformis

Eucalyptus incrassata

Eucalyptus globulus

Eucalyptus erythronema   RED-FLOWERED OR WHITE MALLEE

A mallee or small tree, 4-10 m high often with several slender main stems growing from the rootstock, erect branches and a fairly sparse crown. **Bark** is white, smooth and powdery, pink on the higher branches. **Mature leaves** are alternate, narrow lanceolate, 6-10 cm long and 10-13 mm wide on stalks to 1 cm long, thick and deep green, dotted with oil glands, with a prominent midrib. **Flowers** are red to pink, yellow or cream, about 3 cm across, comprising many stamens spreading from a central disc, and covered by a conical cap in bud, arranged in pendulous clusters of 3-7 flowers on long stalks. **Buds** are club-shaped, about 2 cm long and ribbed. **Fruits** are bell-shaped ribbed woody capsules, about 12 mm long and 13 mm across with 4 valves at rim level. **Flowering** in summer and autumn. **Habitat.** Scattered on clay soils in the wheat country of southwestern WA, cultivated as a street tree in low rainfall areas of the southern states. **Family.** Myrtaceae.

Eucalyptus torquata   CORAL OR COOLGARDIE GUM

A small tree to 12 m high with a straight slender trunk and a dense, broad, rounded crown. **Bark** is dark grey to black, rough and persistent, smooth grey-brown on the smaller branches. **Mature leaves** are alternate, lanceolate, slightly sickle-shaped, 4-15 cm long and 25-30 mm wide on stalks to 15 mm long, dull grey-green with reddish margins and dotted with oil glands, thick with a prominent midrib. **Flowers** are red to pink, white or cream, to 35 mm across, comprising many stamens spreading from a central disc, and covered by a long beaked cap in bud, arranged in pendulous clusters of 2-7 flowers on stalks to 25 mm long. **Buds** are urn-shaped, ribbed with a curved beak, to 25 mm long and 1 cm across. **Fruits** are urn-shaped ribbed woody capsules to 15 mm long with deeply enclosed valves. **Flowering** most of the year. **Habitat.** Native to the Coolgardie district of southern WA, but widely cultivated in the drier parts of Australia. **Family.** Myrtaceae.

Eucalyptus miniata   WOOLLYBUTT

A small to medium-sized tree, 8-30 m high with a cylindrical trunk to 1 m diameter, fairly high branches and a moderately dense spreading crown. **Bark** is grey or rusty red, spongy, fissured, rough and persistent on the lower part of the trunk, shedding in papery flakes higher up to leave a smooth or powdery whitish surface. **Mature leaves** are alternate, lanceolate, sometimes slightly sickle-shaped, 9-16 cm long and 1-5 cm wide with a prominent midrib. **Flowers** are orange or scarlet, to 35 mm across, stalkless or on very short stalks, comprising many stamens spreading from a central disc, and covered by a ribbed hemispherical beaked cap in bud, arranged in axillary or terminal clusters of 3-7 flowers on stout stalks to 35 mm long. **Buds** are ovate to club-shaped and often strongly ribbed, 11-23 mm long and 7-11 mm across with a pointed cap. **Fruits** are cylindrical to ovoid, usually prominently ribbed woody capsules 3-6 cm long and 17-50 mm across with 3 deeply enclosed valves. **Flowering** in winter. **Habitat.** Widely distributed in open forests and woodlands in low tablelands and undulating sandstone country inland in the tropical northern areas of WA, NT and Qld. **Family.** Myrtaceae.

Eucalyptus erythronema

Eucalyptus torquata

Eucalyptus miniata

GLOSSARY

achene: a dry fruit with 1 seed, not splitting open when ripe.

alternate: arranged one by one along a stem, not opposite.

annual: completing its life cycle in one year.

anther: the top end of the stamen, bearing pollen.

aquatic: growing in water.

aromatic: fragrant flowers or foliage.

ascending: growing upwards.

axil: the upper angle between leaf and stem or branch.

axillary: arising from the axil.

bark: outer covering of the stem or root.

beak: pointed projection.

beard: a tuft of hair.

belah (Casuarina cristata): a dominant tree species in some inland areas.

berry: succulent non-opening fruit, usually rounded usually with many seeds.

biennial: completing its life cycle in 2 years.

bipinnate: a leaf twice pinnately divided.

bract: modified leaf often at the base of a flower.

bristle: short stiff hair.

bulb: swollen underground stem, acting as a storage organ.

calli: small, hard protrusions.

calyx: outer whorl of the flower, consisting of sepals.

capsule: dry opening fruit of more than one carpel.

carnivorous: able to trap and digest small animals.

carpel: female part of the flower usually comprising stigma, style and ovary.

clasping: partly or wholly surrounding the stem.

column: structure formed by fused stigmas and styles in orchids.

composite: of the Compositae family, with many florets in a close head surrounded by a common whorl of bracts.

compound: consisting of several similar parts.

compressed: flattened.

cone: a globular collection of fruits around a central axis, surrounded by woody bracts.

conical: cone-shaped.

constricted: drawn together, narrowed as between seeds in a pod.

creeping: remaining close to the ground.

cypsella: a dry, single seeded fruit, not splitting open on maturity.

decumbent: lying on the ground with the tip turned up.

decussate: leaves arranged opposite in pairs at right angles.

depressed: flattened or sunken.

downy: with short soft hairs.

drupe: fleshy non-opening fruit with a hard kernel and solitary seed.

elliptical: a plane surface shaped like an ellipse.

entire: a margin without teeth or lobes.

epiphyte: a plant growing on another plant or object, using it for support and not nourishment.

family: a group of closely related genera.

filament: stalk bearing the anther.

floral leaves: leaves immediately below the flowers.

floret: one of the small flowers in a compact head.

flower: sexual reproductive structure.

follicle: a dry fruit formed from 1 carpel, splitting open along the inner margin.

fruit: seed-bearing part of a plant.

genus: a group of closely related species.

gland: embedded or projecting structure usually secreting oil, nectar, resin or water.

globular: globe-shaped, spherical or nearly so.

habitat: natural abode of a plant.

head: dense cluster of stalkless flowers.

heath: an area occupied mainly by low, shrubby plants, whose growth is conditioned by severe environmental factors.

herb: a plant that does not have a woody stem.

inflorescence: arrangment of the flowers of a plant.

keel: the two lower fused petals of a pea-like flower.

kino: red or black juice or gum.

labellum: the modified lip-like petal of orchid flowers.

lanceolate: lance-shaped, tapering at each end, broadest below the middle, about four times as long as broad.

lateral: on the side or edge.

leaf: usually a green flat organ attached to the stem, manufacturing food.

leaflet: a secondary part of a compound leaf.
linear: long and narrow.
lip: one of the petals or sepals of the flower.
lobe: rounded or pointed division of a leaf; the sepal or petal of a flower.

mallee: Eucalypts growing with several stunted stems, common in arid and alpine areas.
margin: edge of a leaf or other organ.
midrib: main vein of a leaf running from base to tip.

nut: a dry non-opening fruit with one seed and hard woody covering.

oblong: having roughly parallel sides, longer than broad with a rounded tip.
obovate: almost ovate, but broader towards the tip.
opposite: in pairs one at each side of the stem.
orbicular: more or less circular in outline.
ovate: egg-shaped, broadest below the middle.
ovary: female structure enclosing the unfertilised seeds.
ovoid: an egg-shaped solid body.

palmate: a leaf divided into three or more leaflets or lobes arising from a common point.
panicle: a much-branched inflorescence.
perennial: a plant living for more than two years.
petal: a segment of the inner whorl of the floral lobes.
phyllode: flattened leaf stalk resembling and acting as a leaf.
pinnate: a compound leaf with leaflets on opposite side of a common leaf stalk.
pod: dry, opening, multi-seeded fruit.
pollen: powdery substance produced in the anthers.
prostrate: lying on the ground.
pseudo-bulb: swollen bulb-like part of the stem of many epiphytic orchids.

raceme: an infloresence with stalked flowers borne along an unbranched axis.
ray: outer flattened flower in the Compositae.
regular: radially symmetrical.
riverine: situated beside a river.

saprophyte: an organism using non-living organic matter for food.
scale: very small rudimentary leaf, or flat closely pressed leaf.
scattered: leaves arranged in a random manner along the stem.
sclerophyll: plants with harsh-textured, tough leaves.

scrambling: climbing with the help of backward-pointing hooked spines.
scrub: a community dominated by shrubs.
sepal: a segment of the outer whorl of the flower.
serrate: a leaf margin with many sharp teeth, as on a saw.
shrub: a woody, perennial plant with several stems growing from the base, without a single trunk as in a tree.
silky: covered with fine soft hair.
spathulate: shaped like a spatula, tapering from a rounded tip to a narrow base.
species: a group of individual plants essentially alike when grown under similar conditions, normally breeding freely with others of their own kind: the basic unit of biological classification.
spherical: in the form of a globe.
spike: a compact inflorescence of stalkless flowers.
stamen: male part of a flower comprising filament and anther.
standard: broad posterior petal in a pea-shaped flower.
stigma: receptive tip of the style.
stipule: one of a pair of scale or leaf-like appendages at the base of a leaf.
style: stalk arising from the ovary and bearing the stigma.
succulent: soft and juicy.
synonym (syn.): a plant name set aside in favour of an earlier one.

tepal: petal or sepal, being scarcely distinguishable from each other.
terminal: at the apex.
terrestrial: plants growing in the ground, not aquatic or epiphytic.
tessellated: in the form of small squares.
throat: the opening of the flowering tube.
tree: a perennial plant with a single woody trunk and distinct head or crown.
trifoliolate: having 3 leaflets.
twining: climbing by coiling the stem around the support.
tufted: stems or leaves growing close together.

valve: a cell or compartment in a fully matured capsule.
vein: visible appearance of vascular tissue in a leaf.
whorl: a group of three or more structures encircling an axis at the same level.
wing: the membranous extension of a seed or fruit; the two lateral petals of a pea-shaped flower.
woolly: having long, soft, matted hair.

LEAF SHAPES

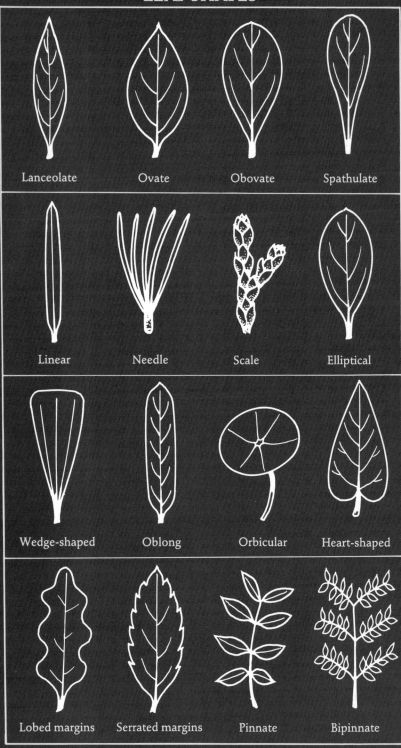

Lanceolate	Ovate	Obovate	Spathulate
Linear	Needle	Scale	Elliptical
Wedge-shaped	Oblong	Orbicular	Heart-shaped
Lobed margins	Serrated margins	Pinnate	Bipinnate

FLOWER PARTS AND LEAF ARRANGEMENTS

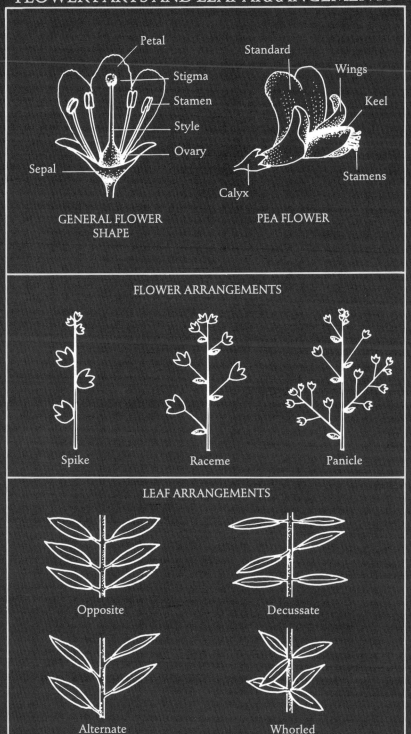

GENERAL FLOWER SHAPE

Petal
Stigma
Stamen
Style
Ovary
Sepal

PEA FLOWER

Standard
Wings
Keel
Stamens
Calyx

FLOWER ARRANGEMENTS

Spike

Raceme

Panicle

LEAF ARRANGEMENTS

Opposite

Decussate

Alternate

Whorled

REFERENCES

Anderson, R.H., *The Trees of New South Wales*. NSW Dept. of Agriculture, Govt. Printer, Sydney, 1939-1968.

Beadle, N.C.W., Evans, O.D. and Carolin, R.C., *Flora of the Sydney Region*. Reed Books, Sydney, 1982.

Beadle, N.C.W. et al., *Handbook of the Vascular Plants of the Sydney District and the Blue Mountains*. Self published, Armidale, NSW, 1962.

Beadle, N.C.W., *Students Flora of North Eastern New South Wales*. Vols I-V. Dept. of Botany, University of New England, Armidale, NSW, 1971-1984.

Black, J.M., *Flora of South Australia*. Parts I-IV. Govt. Printer, Adelaide, 1948-1960.

Blackall, W.E., *How to Know Western Australian Wildflowers*. Vols. I-III. University of WA Press, 1965.

Blakely, W.F., *A Key to the Eucalypts*. 2nd Ed. Forestry and Timber Bureau, Canberra, 1955.

Boland, D.J. et al., *Forest Trees of Australia*. Thomas Nelson and CSIRO, Melbourne, 1985.

Burbidge, N.T. and Gray, M., *Flora of the ACT*. Australian National University Press, Canberra, 1970.

Bureau of Flora and Fauna, *Flora of Australia*. Vols. 8, 22, 25, 45 and 46. Govt. Publishing Service, Canberra, 1981-87.

Cameron, M. (ed.), *Guide to Flowers and Plants of Tasmania*. Reed Books, Sydney, 1984.

Costermans, L., *Native Trees and Shrubs of South-eastern Australia*. Rigby Publishers, Sydney, 1981.

Curtis, W.M. and Morris, D.I., *The Student's Flora of Tasmania*. Parts I-II. 2nd Ed. Govt. Printer, Tasmania, 1975.

Elliot, W.R. and Jones, D.L., *Encyclopaedia of Australian Plants Suitable for Cultivation*. Vols. II, III, and IV. Lothian, Melbourne, 1986.

Ewart, A.J., *Flora of Victoria*. Vict. Govt. University Press, 1931.

Floyd, A.G., *Index of New South Wales Rainforest Trees*. Parts I-XII. Forestry Commission of NSW, Sydney, 1984.

Francis, W.D., *Australian Rainforest Trees*. Govt. Publishing Service, 1981.

Fuller, L., *Wollongong's Native Trees*. Weston & Co., Kiama, NSW, 1982.

Gardner, C.A., *Eucalypts of Western Australia*. WA Dept. of Agriculture, 1979.

Harris, T.Y., *Alpine Plants of Australia*. Angus and Robertson, Sydney, 1970.

Hockings, F.D. and Daniels, C.A., *The Australian Gardener's Guide to Flowering Shrubs*. Reed Books, Sydney, 1982.

Holliday, I. and Hill, R., *A Field Guide to Australian Trees*. Rigby Publishers, Adelaide, 1984.

Holliday, I. and Watton, G., *A Field Guide to Banksias*. Rigby Publishers, Adelaide, 1975.

Holliday, I. and Watton, G., *A Gardener's Guide to Eucalypts*. Rigby Publishers, Adelaide, 1983.

Jacobs, S.W.L. and Pickard, J., *Plants of NSW, A Census of Cycads, Conifers and Angiosperms*, Royal Botanical Gardens, Sydney, 1981 (updated).

Jessop, J. (ed.), *Flora of Central Australia*. Reed Books, Sydney, 1981.

Jessop, J. and Toelken, H.R., *Flora of South Australia*. Vols I-IV. SA Govt. Printing Division, Adelaide, 1986.

Jones, D.L., *Ornamental Rainforest Plants in Australia*. Reed Books, Sydney, 1986.

Kelly, S. (ed.), *Eucalypts*. Thomas Nelson, Melbourne, 1983.

Millet, M. and Hosel, J., *Native Trees of Australia*. Lansdowne Press, Sydney, 1971.

Morley, B.D. and Toelken, H.R. (eds.), *Flowering Plants of Australia*. Rigby Publishers, Adelaide, 1983.

Rowell, R., *Ornamental Flowering Trees in Australia*. Reed Books, Sydney, 1980.

Simpfendorfer, K.J., *An Introduction to the Trees of South Eastern Australia*. Inkata Press, Melbourne, 1975.

Stanley, T.D. and Ross, E.M.,*Flora of South-eastern Queensland*. Vols I and II. Qld Dept. of Primary Industries, 1981.

INDEX

BOTANICAL NAMES

INDEX

COMMON NAMES